The Best Of Teacher's Helper®
Reproducibles And Activities For Your Classroom
Math
Kindergarten

W9-BZC-142

Editor in Chief
Margaret Michel

Manager, Product Development
Charlotte Perkins

Manager, Magazines Division
Julie Peck

Editors
Jennifer L. Overend
Kathy Wolf

Contributing Writers
Jane Fittante, Lucia Kemp Henry, Valerie Lathrop, Beth Schimmel,
Charlene Shidisky, Jan Trautman

Copy Editors
Debbié Blaylock
Gina Sutphin

Artists
Jennifer T. Bennett, Pam Crane, Teresa Davidson, Barry Slate,
Rebecca Saunders, Donna Teal

Cover Artist
Cathy Spangler Bruce

Typographer
Lynette Maxwell

©1994 by THE EDUCATION CENTER, INC.
All rights reserved except as here noted.
ISBN# 1-56234-107-3

Manufactured in the United States
10 9 8 7 6 5 4

Table Of Contents

Name

Slither In A Circle

Trace.

 Color the ◯s.

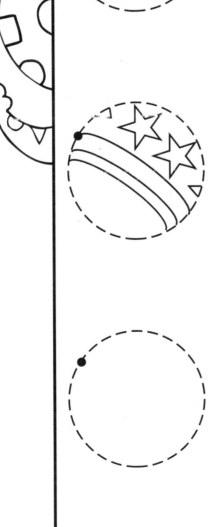

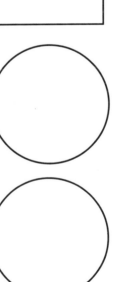

Note To The Teacher

Each sheet in this unit provides opportunities for the child to trace the shape featured on each page and then identify that same shape from an assortment of shapes and color the featured shape. In order to provide the opportunity to freely draw the shapes, fun sheets are featured on pages 6 and 8. These sheets could be cut in half and even duplicated on the backs of the corresponding shape worksheet when you duplicate it so the child will have the activity on the back of his worksheet to complete as each shape is covered.

Follow-Up Activity

Have fun with Shapely the Snake in this unit. Provide each child with an 18-inch length of rope or heavy yarn. Provide two simple head shapes (see pattern below) to be glued to one end of the yarn (sandwiching the yarn between). As you introduce each shape, allow the children to practice using Shapely to make the shape on their desks. This tactile, hands-on experience before moving to the worksheet will help increase success on the worksheets.

Patterns

©The Education Center, Inc. • TEC880

©The Education Center, Inc. • TEC880

©The Education Center, Inc. • TEC880

©The Education Center, Inc. • TEC880

Shapely Snake's Squares

Trace.

 Color the ☐ s.

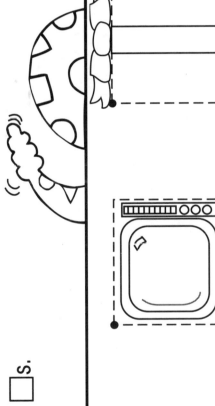

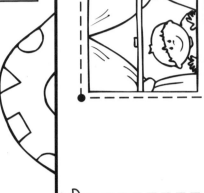

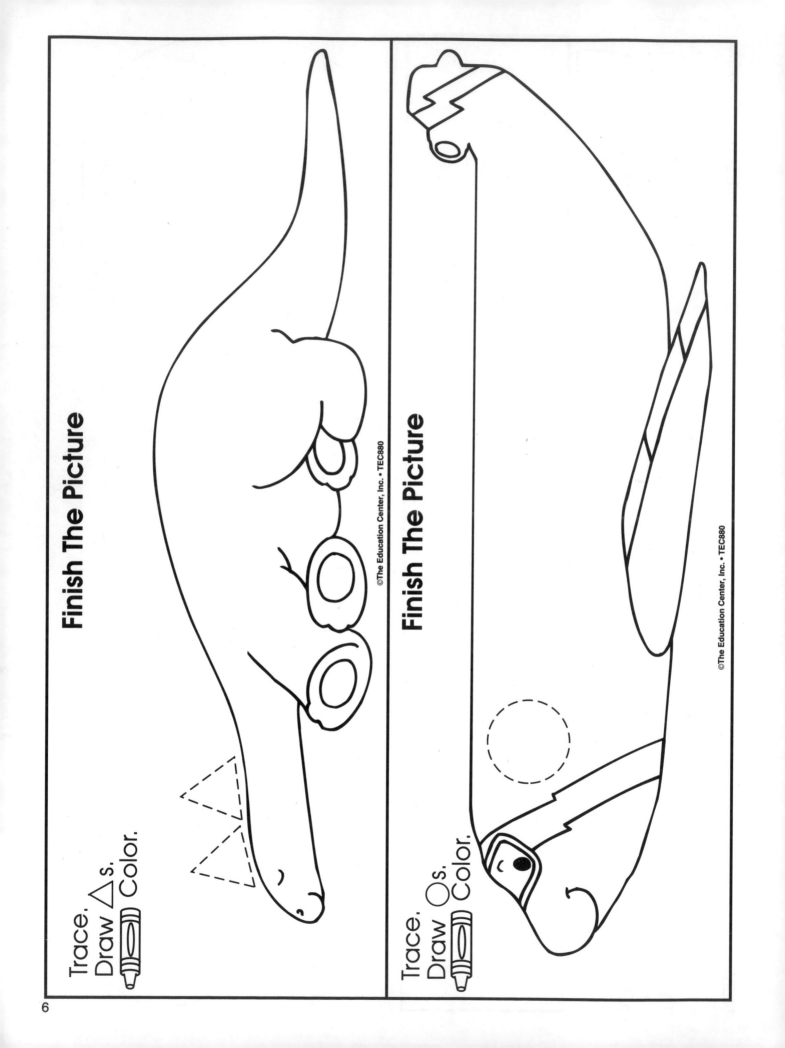

Finish The Picture

Trace.
Draw △s.
Color.

©The Education Center, Inc. • TEC880

Finish The Picture

Trace.
Draw ○s.
Color.

©The Education Center, Inc. • TEC880

Name

Rectangle Reptile

Trace.

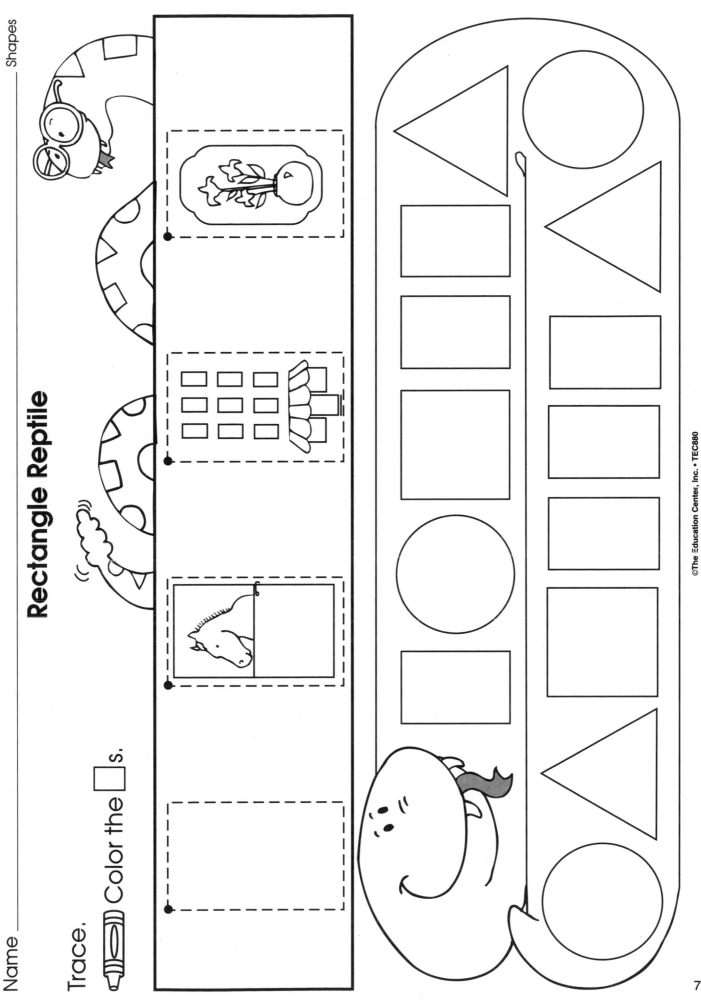

Color the ▭ s.

Finish The Picture

Trace.

Draw ☐s.

 Color.

Finish The Picture

Trace.

Draw ☐ ▭ s.

 Color.

Name _____

Shapely Strikes Again

Trace.

🖍 Color the △s.

Spiders Love Shapes!

Cut.

Paste.

Circle	Square	Triangle

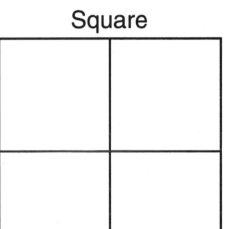 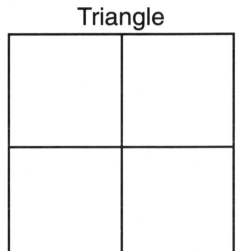

11

Extension Activity
Spiders And Shapes

These spiders just love shapes! With this activity, your students can fill their spiders' webs with lots of shapes. Duplicate student copies of the web on page 14 and the spider pattern and shape cards below. Have each child color and cut out her spider and her web. Next have each child color her shapes as follows: circles—red, triangles—blue, squares—green, and rectangles—yellow. Then have the child cut out the shape cards and glue them as desired on the spider web. Suspend each child's spider from its web with a length of yarn and mount the completed projects to a bulletin-board display entitled "We Love Spiders And Shapes!"

Spider Pattern

©The Education Center, Inc.

Shape Cards

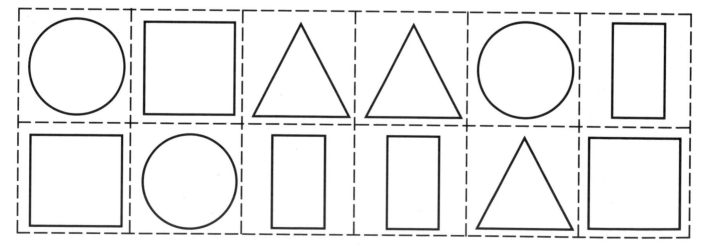

©The Education Center, Inc. • TEC880

Spider Doodles

Trace.

Color the shapes that match.

Variation

Page 13 can be used two ways. The children may color the one shape in each row which is identical in size, shape, and orientation to the first dashed shape. As a variation, the children may color all the figures which are the same as the first one, regardless of their sizes and orientations.

Web Pattern

Use with "Spiders And Shapes" on page 12.

Finished Project

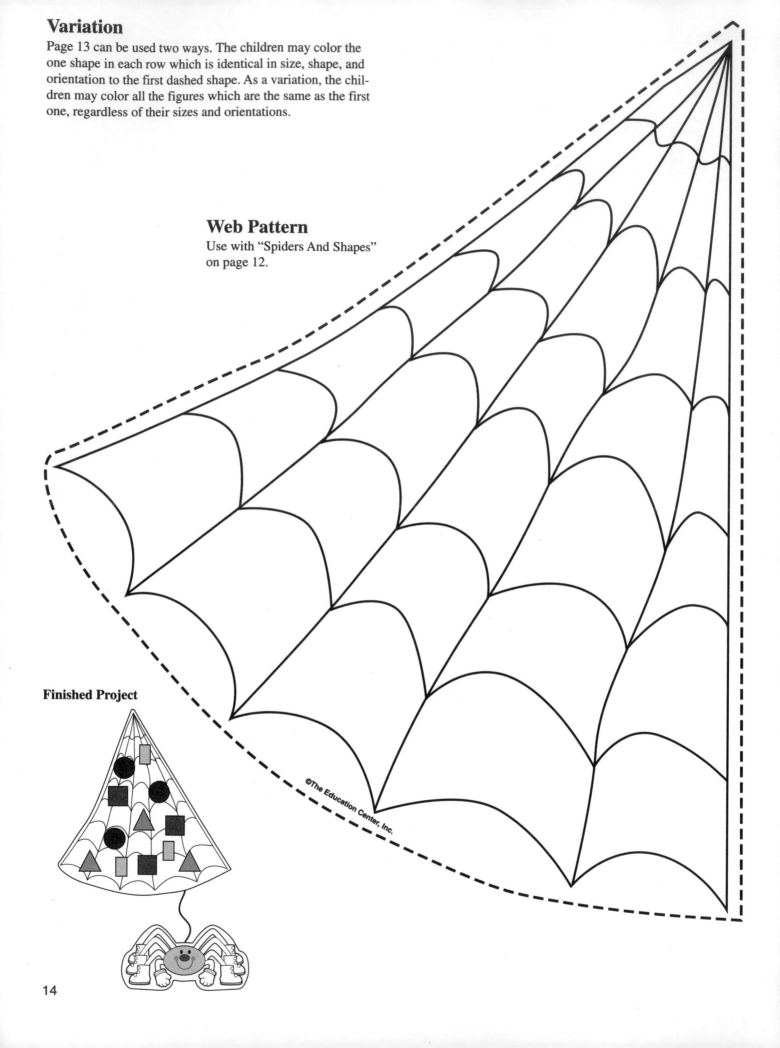

14

Shapely Spiders

 Cut.  Paste. Trace.  Draw.

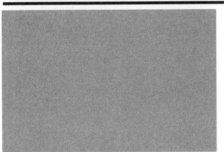  

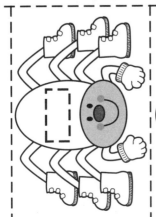  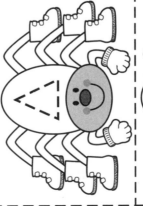 

Colorful Clown Face

 Color the numerals by the code.

 **Color Code**

1	2	3	4	5	6	7
red	yellow	blue	green	orange	purple	brown

How To Use This Sheet

1. Call attention to the color code at the bottom of this sheet.
2. One by one, name each numeral and the color word beneath the numeral.
3. Allow the children to color each color-word box the appropriate color as you identify its color word.
4. Once all color-code boxes have been named and colored, each child should complete the worksheet independently by coloring the numbered spaces on the clown according to the code.
5. Remind children to color lightly to avoid obliterating the numerals.

Name _____

Plenty Of Pickles

Look at each pickle.

 Color green if numbers are the **same**.

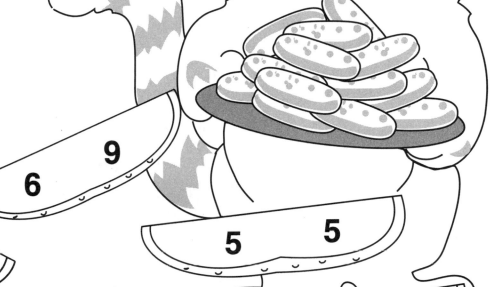

8   8

1   6   9
7

5   5

3   8   2   2
10   10

9   4   4   5
9   6

10   0   1   1

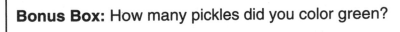
©The Education Center, Inc. • TEC880

19

Extension Activity
Pickle Power

This activity helps your youngsters practice identifying numerals. Duplicate a set of pickle cards below on green construction paper for each child. Use the duplicating machine to enlarge one set of pickle cards for you. Have students cut out their cards and position them faceup on their desks. To play, display one of the enlarged pickle cards for the children. Have each child identify the matching card on his desk and hold it up for you to see. Continue in this manner until students have identified all of the numerals. After playing, clip each set of cards together and store them in an empty pickle jar. Culminate the activity by providing slices of various kinds of pickles for students to sample.

Pickle Cards

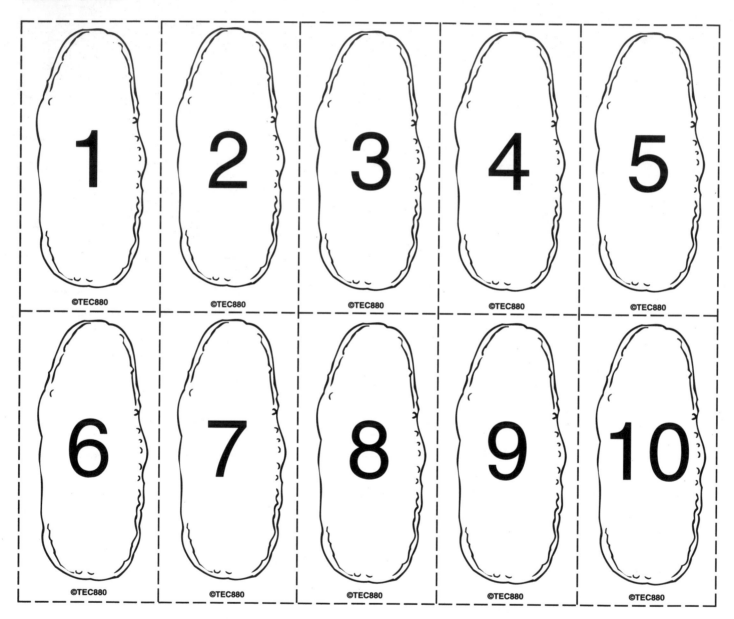

©TEC880 ©TEC880 ©TEC880 ©TEC880 ©TEC880

©TEC880 ©TEC880 ©TEC880 ©TEC880 ©TEC880

In A Pickle

Look at the ⬭ .

Match.

Circle.

Pickles

3	8	5	3
9	9	6	0
4	5	4	2
7	1	10	7
1	4	1	7
8	8	3	6
0	10	8	0
5	5	6	2
10	01	10	0
2	3	2	5
6	8	9	6

Apple Harvest

Listen and do.

23

Oral Instructions

1. Find the apples. Color the **big** apple **red.**
2. Circle the **long** wagon.
3. Make an X on the **big** crate.
4. Color the **tall** basket **brown.**
5. Draw a line under the **short** tree.
6. Color the **small** cloud **blue.**
7. Draw one **yellow** apple on the **tall** tree.
8. Color the **thin** worm **green.**
9. Circle the **small** butterfly.
10. Draw a bird nest in the **short** tree.
11. Draw a picture of you playing!

Name _____

Apple Pie Slices!

Group 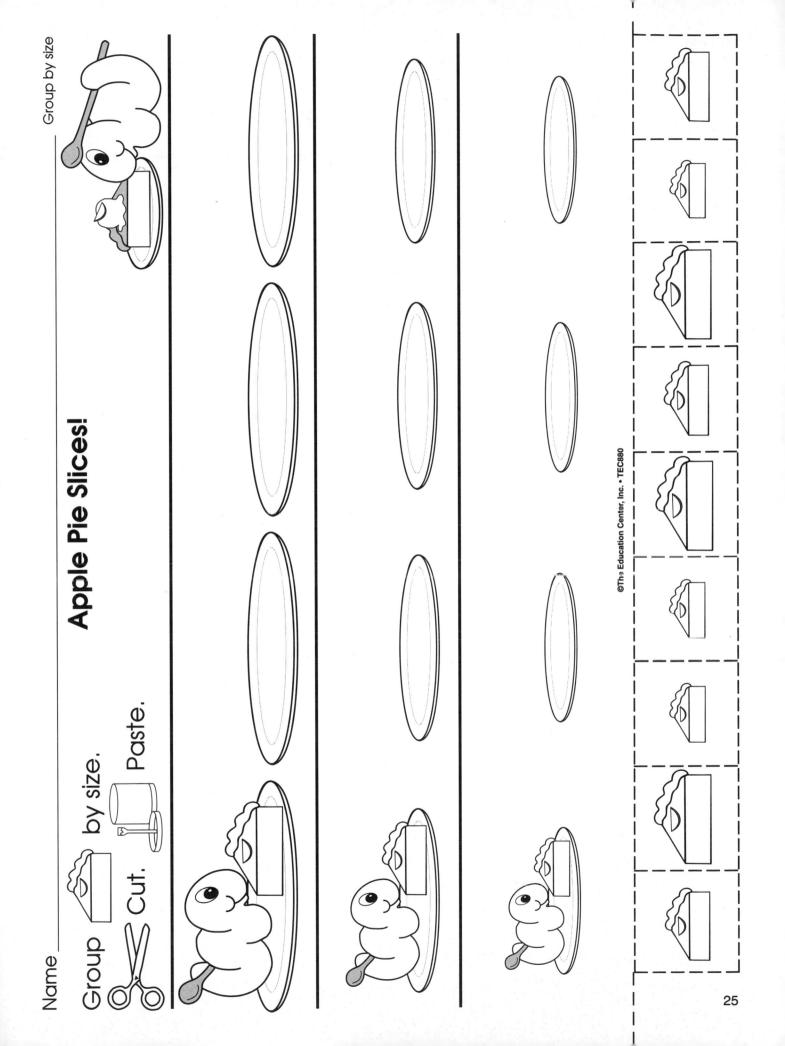 by size.

Cut.

Paste.

Award

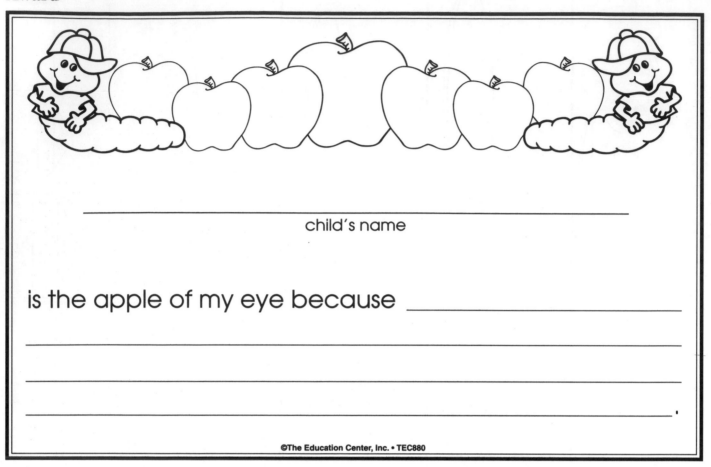

_____
child's name

is the apple of my eye because _____

_____

_____

_____.

Creative Patterns

 Cut.

Create patterns:

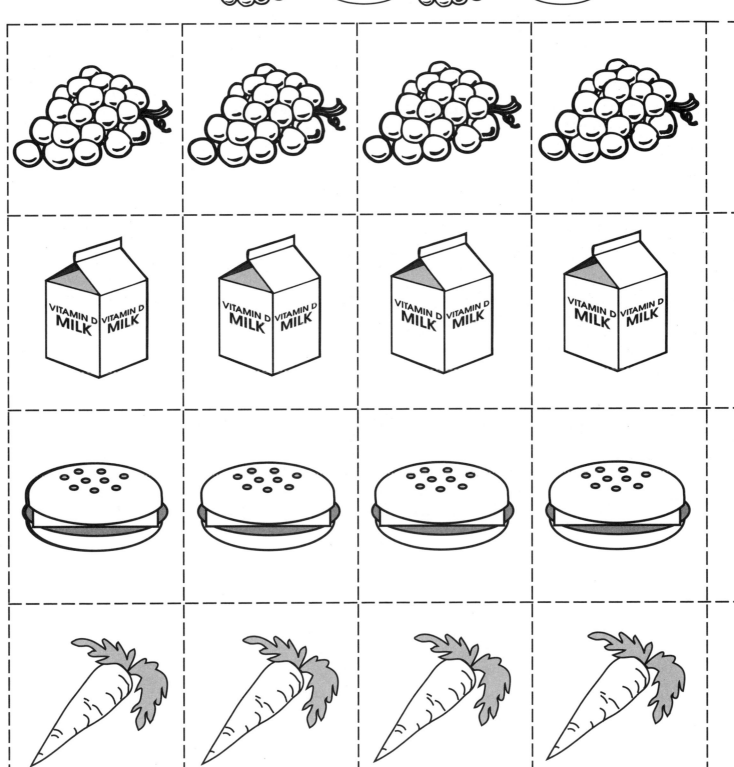

How To Use This Sheet

1. Duplicate this sheet for each child.
2. Allow the children to cut the sheet into individual food pieces by cutting on the dotted lines.
3. Encourage the children to use the food pieces to create patterns like the example at the top of the worksheet.
4. Send the food pieces home in a Ziploc® plastic bag with the parent note below for continued learning!

Variations

— Duplicate page 27 on white construction paper. Color the food pictures. Laminate and cut apart. Place flannel tape or magnetic tape on the backs of the pieces for repeated use on a flannel or magnetic board.

— Allow the children to paste the pieces to a sheet of drawing paper as they create patterns.

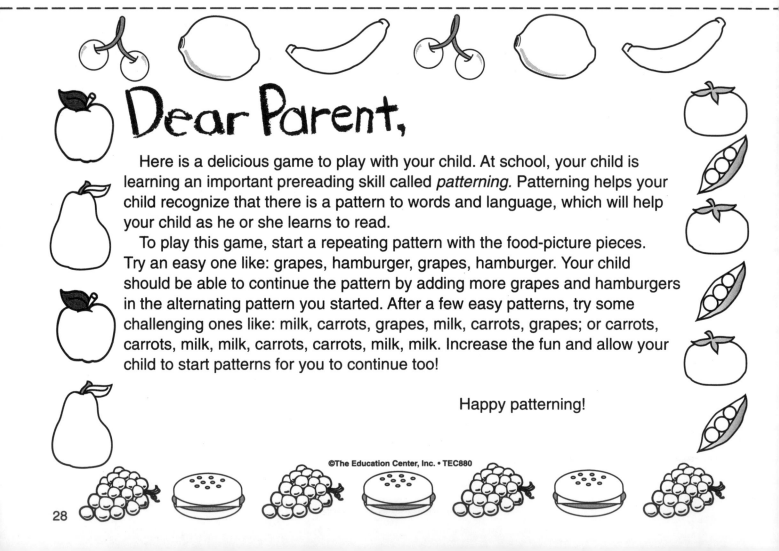

Dear Parent,

Here is a delicious game to play with your child. At school, your child is learning an important prereading skill called *patterning*. Patterning helps your child recognize that there is a pattern to words and language, which will help your child as he or she learns to read.

To play this game, start a repeating pattern with the food-picture pieces. Try an easy one like: grapes, hamburger, grapes, hamburger. Your child should be able to continue the pattern by adding more grapes and hamburgers in the alternating pattern you started. After a few easy patterns, try some challenging ones like: milk, carrots, grapes, milk, carrots, grapes; or carrots, carrots, milk, milk, carrots, carrots, milk, milk. Increase the fun and allow your child to start patterns for you to continue too!

Happy patterning!

Yummy Patterns

Color what comes next.

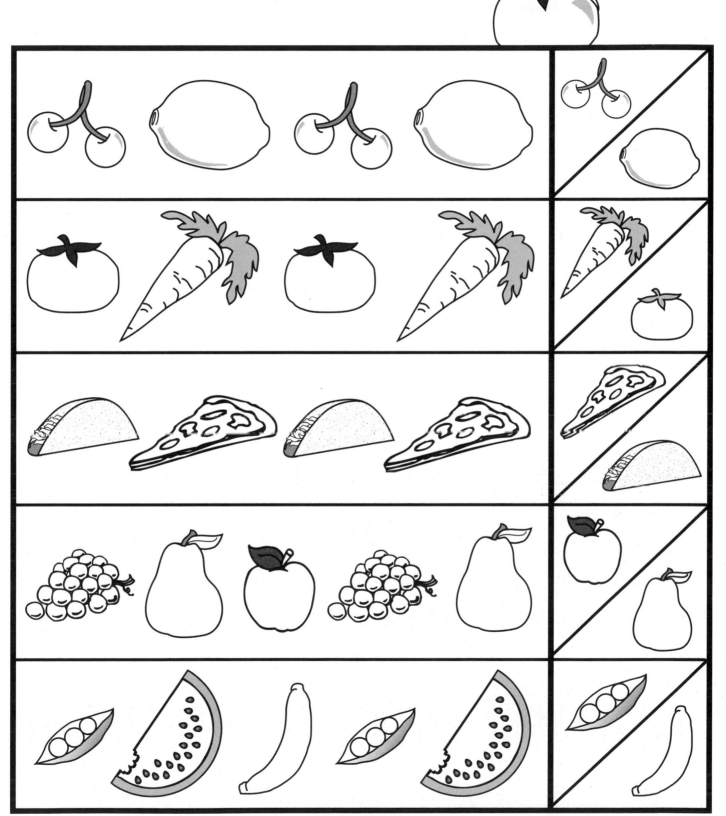

Name _____

Candy Kiss Counting

Trace.

Count.

Color.

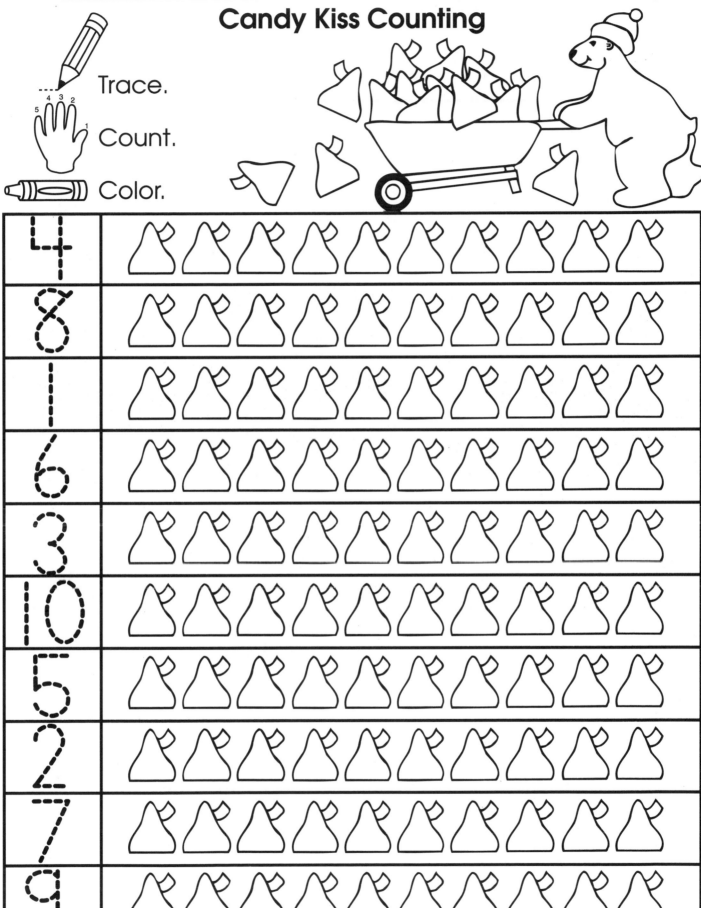

Follow-Up Activity

Have fun with estimation with this counting candy unit. Obtain a glass jar and your favorite type of candy. Fill the jar with the candy. Allow the children to guess how many pieces of candy they think are in the jar. List the children's guesses on a chart. Count the candy with your children and see who came the closest!

Name _____

Colorful Candy

Count.

Color: 1 ◌ red   5 ◌ purple
        2 ◌ yellow   6 ◌ green
        3 ◌ black   7 ◌ orange
        4 ◌ blue   8 ◌ brown

How many s are left? _____

Extension Activity
Candy Sorting

Duplicate student copies of the candy cards below and the candy jar on page 36. Have students cut out the candy cards and sort them into matching groups. Then have the child color the candy in each group the same color. Next have the child glue the candy cards to the jar. This activity can also be done using real candy, but be sure that children do not try to eat the candy that has been glued to the jar.

Candy Cards

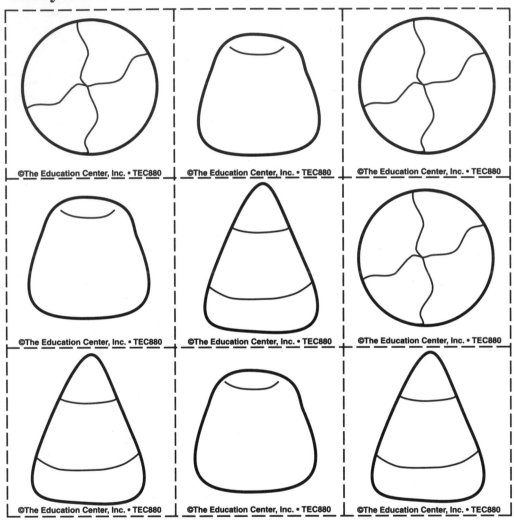

©The Education Center, Inc. • TEC880

©The Education Center, Inc. • TEC880

©The Education Center, Inc. • TEC880

©The Education Center, Inc. • TEC880

©The Education Center, Inc. • TEC880

©The Education Center, Inc. • TEC880

©The Education Center, Inc. • TEC880

©The Education Center, Inc. • TEC880

©The Education Center, Inc. • TEC880

Name _____

Sweet Tooth

 Count s.

 Cut teeth .

Paste to match.

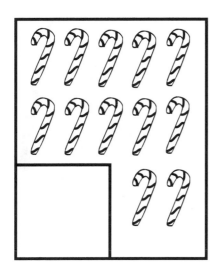

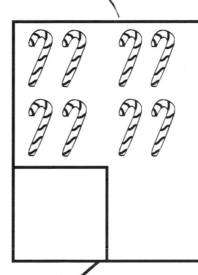

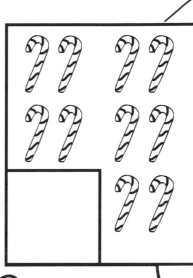

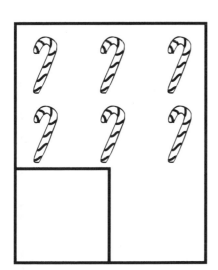

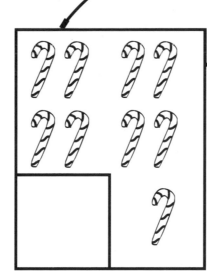

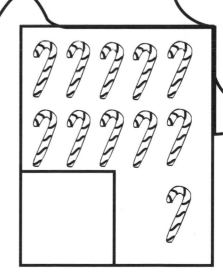

| 6 | 7 | 8 | 9 | 10 | 11 | 12 |

Jar Pattern

Use with "Candy Sorting" on page 34.

Name _____

The Candy Shop

Count.

Circle the numeral.

10	**11**	**12**
13	**14**	**15**
8	**9**	**10**
11	**12**	**13**
11	**12**	**13**
12	**13**	**14**
13	**14**	**15**
10	**11**	**12**
9	**10**	**11**
12	**13**	**14**

Extension Activity
Candy Graphing

Duplicate student copies of the candy graph below. Prepare a plastic sandwich bag for each child filled with two to six of the following candies: M&Ms®, Gummy Bears®, candy corn, and chocolate chips. To begin, each child empties the contents of his bag on his desk. Then each child sorts his candies according to kind. To complete the graph, the child begins with the first row and draws an M&M for each M&M that he has on his desk. Then the child counts the total number of candies in that row and writes the numeral in the space provided. The child continues in this manner until each row of the graph is complete.

Name		
Candy	Draw candy in straight line here.	Total
m		
(gummy bear)		
(candy corn)		
(chocolate chip)		

Name

Harvesttime

Listen and do.

Oral Instructions

1. Color two baskets brown.
2. Draw five flowers in the garden by Farmer Fred.
3. Color seven carrots orange.
4. Circle the corn plant with nine ears of corn.
5. Make an X on the lettuce pile that has three heads of lettuce.
6. Draw one pocket on Farmer Fred's overalls.
7. Circle six onions.
8. Color eight of the tomatoes red.
9. Draw four wheels on Farmer Fred's wagon.
10. Count the seeds in the watermelons. Mark an X on the watermelon that has ten seeds.

Extension Activities
Harvesttime/Counting

— A simple counting game can be made quickly with an egg carton and some dried beans. Cover the top of the egg carton with self-adhesive paper. In the bottom of each egg cup, write a numeral from one to 12 with a permanent marker. Provide beans (at least 78). The children can practice counting the beans into the egg cups according to the number at the bottom of each cup. When each child is done playing, all that's necessary to clean up is to close the carton and gently shake—it's ready for the next player.

— Make some seedy number puzzles. Cut twelve 4 1/2-inch-by-6-inch cards from oaktag (you can get four from each sheet of 9-inch-by-12-inch oaktag). Write one numeral from one to 12 on the bottom half of each card. Glue a variety of seed types in sets to the top of each card to match the numeral on the bottom of the card. Cut the cards apart puzzle-style. The children may then count the seeds and match the piece to the numeral. This game will also provide a wonderful tactile experience as the children feel the seeds as they count.

— Make a class seed graph! Provide three different kinds of seeds (pumpkin, bean, and corn are easily recognized). Divide a poster board into a grid with three columns and enough rows for all your children. Glue one of each kind of seed to the bottom of a column to label the column. Allow each child to choose his favorite seed and glue it in the correct column. After all the children have had a chance to choose and glue their seeds, talk about the graph. Which seed was chosen the most? The least? Are any of the columns equal? How many more pumpkin seeds than corn seeds were chosen?

Seed Graph		
Pumpkin	**Bean**	**Corn**
🎃		
🎃		🌽
🎃	🫘	🌽
🎃	🫘	🌽
🎃	🫘	🌽
🎃	🫘	🌽

Name _____

Farmer Fred's Counting Fun

Listen and do.

Color.

Cut.

©The Education Center, Inc.

©The Education Center, Inc. • TEC880

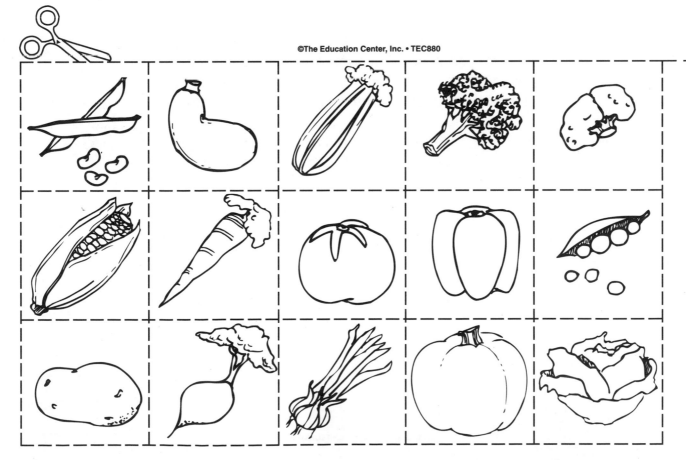

How To Use Page 41

1. Each child will need to bring in a margarine tub (the small size works best, but any size will work).
2. Have the children color the picture of Farmer Fred in the circle and cut the circle out.
3. Staple or glue the circle to the cover of the margarine tub.
4. Have the children color and cut out the vegetable pieces at the bottom of the page. Name the vegetables to help build vocabulary.
5. To play this counting game, give verbal directions for counting the vegetables into the tub. For example: "Let's help Farmer Fred count his vegetable harvest. Count eight vegetables into your tub. Now add two more vegetables to your tub. How many vegetables are left? Put the remaining five vegetables in the tub." Dump the vegetables out and repeat many times with varying directions until interest wanes.
6. Send home with the parent note below for continued learning.

Variation

If you can't obtain the margarine tubs, simply color and cut out the picture of Farmer Fred and his vegetables and place them in a Ziploc® bag to store the pieces. Then, instead of placing the vegetables in the tub, simply "give" the vegetables to Farmer Fred by placing the vegetables on his circle.

Dear Parent,

Take a few moments to play an easy counting game with your child. Your child has helped Farmer Fred bring in the harvest. We have been working on counting at school, and this game helps make it more fun. Ask your child to give a certain number of vegetables (from one to 15) to Farmer Fred. Listen while your child counts. Help him or her name the vegetables too!

Switch roles with your child and let him or her tell you how many vegetables to give to Farmer Fred. Try fooling your child by counting too many or too few, and let your child decide how many to take away or add to make the number he or she gave you correct.

Try some simple addition after you have played awhile. For example, ask your child to count five vegetables, and then ask him or her to add two more. Ask how many there are altogether, and count the vegetables to find out.

Happy counting!

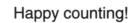

Name _____

Popping Good Counting

Trace.

Glue .

3	10	5	8	2
4	6	-----	9	7

Bonus Box: Cut the number cards apart. On construction paper, glue them in order from 1–10.

©The Education Center, Inc. • TEC880

43

How To Use This Sheet

1. Duplicate this sheet on construction paper for sturdiness.
2. Provide unpopped popcorn kernels and glue.
3. The children trace the numeral in each box and then glue the corresponding number of popcorn kernels in each box.
4. For an additional challenge—after the glue has dried—cut the boxes apart to form tactile number cards. Have the children place the cards in number order.

Name _____

Count Those Carrots

 Count.

 Color.

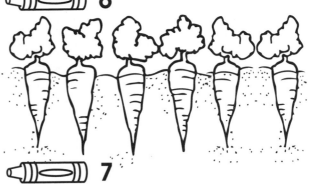

4

6

2

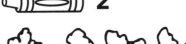

7

10

5

Bonus Box: Draw and color a picture of your favorite vegetable on the back.

Peas In A Pod

Name _____

Count the ◯s.

Circle the number.

Color the ◯s.

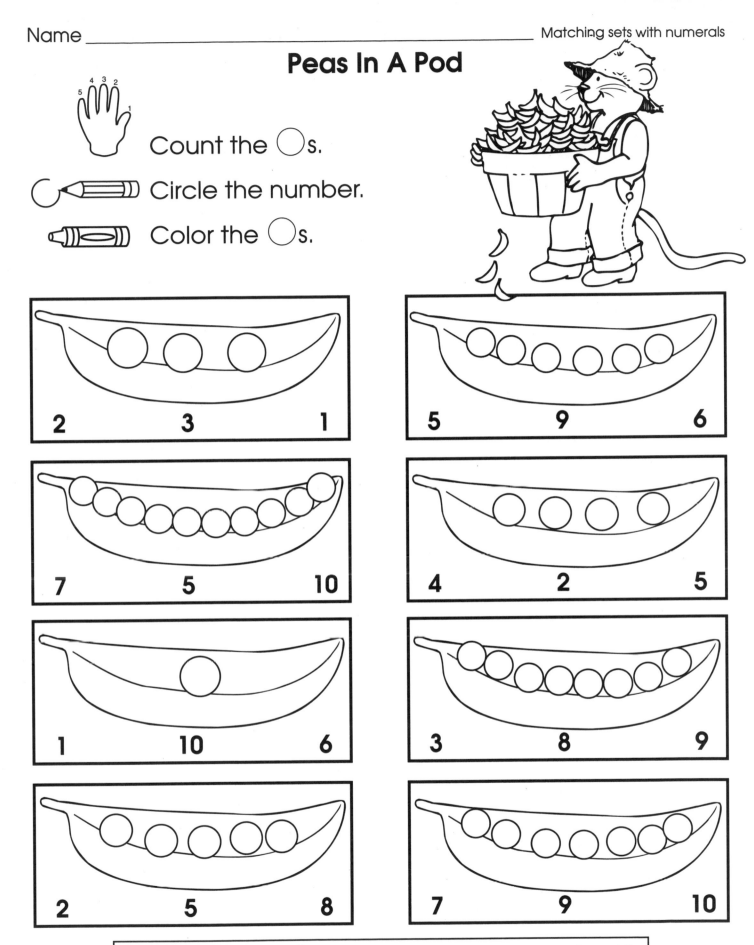

Bonus Box: Make pea pod pictures on the back to match 2 and 9.

The Chip Set

Color.

Cut.

Play.

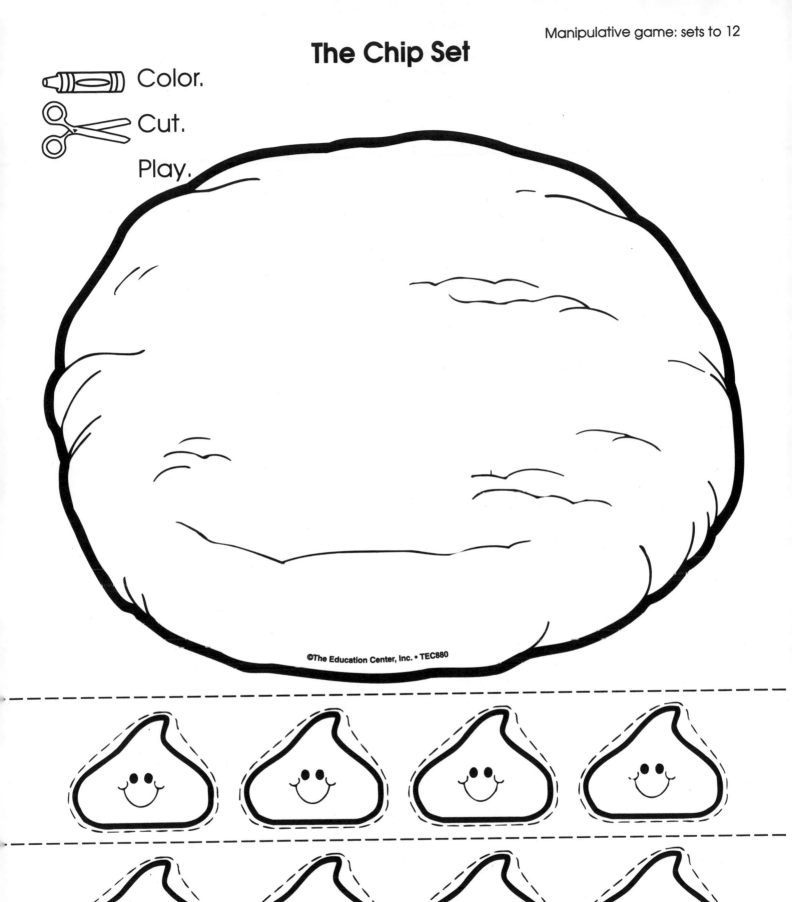

How To Use Pages 49 and 51

1. Reproduce pages 49 and 51 on light brown construction paper for sturdiness. Cut off the parent note and reserve it to send home with the finished game. Color the chips brown. Cut out the big cookie, chips, and numeral cards. Sort the numerals and chips into two piles. Place the chips in a line and count them, pointing to each chip as it is counted. Place the numerals in a horizontal line in numerical order. (Demonstrate to be sure that the numerals read from left to right.) Give help freely. Name each numeral out loud. Let the students point as you name random numerals.

2. Play the game. Ask the children to place the cookie right in front of them. Tell them that they will play a game with number sets. Ask the children to locate the numeral two in the row of cut-out numerals. Place it above the cookie. Then make a set of two chips on the cookie. Check to be sure that everyone has the idea. Replace the chips and numeral in their original positions. Repeat with other numerals and sets.

3. Send the pieces home in a Ziploc® bag with the parent note on page 51 for continued practice.

Variation

After some play as directed above, children can play independently. Tell the children to turn all of the numeral cards upside down. To play, a numeral card is turned up and identified. That number of chips should be placed on the cookie.

Extension Activity

While working with this unit, you might decide to put measuring skills to use with a cooking activity.

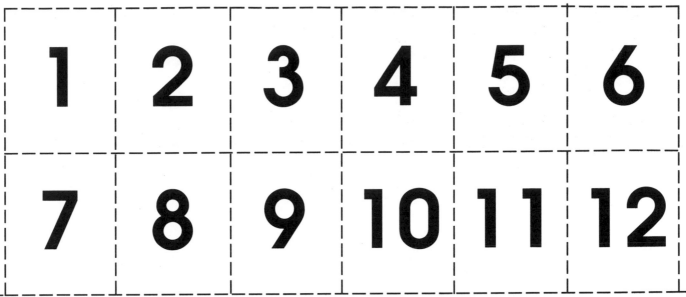

1	2	3	4	5	6
7	8	9	10	11	12

Dear Parent,

We have been having delicious fun with math skills at school! In this game, you and your child can practice making number sets to 12. To play the game, turn all of the numeral cards facedown on a table. Place the large cookie and the chips in front of your child. Allow your child to turn over a card, identify the numeral on the card, and count that many chips onto the cookie.

For an additional challenge, use only the numeral cards one through six. Turn these cards facedown. Turn over any two cards. Use chips to make the two that correspond to the two numeral cards. Make the two sets distinct by forming them onto the far left and right of the cookie. Ask your child how many chips there are altogether in the two sets. By playing this way, you are working on counting as well as beginning addition concepts.

Have a delicious time!

Sincerely,

Pastry Play

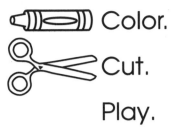

Color.

Cut.

Play.

Additional Materials Needed

— two small paper plates or 2 six-inch construction-paper circles for each child

How To Use Page 53

1. Duplicate page 53 on construction paper for sturdiness.
2. Let the children describe the pictures. Count the cupcakes together. Count the doughnuts together. Color and cut out the pieces on the dotted lines. Distribute the plates or construction-paper circles.
3. Direct the children to sort the baked goods into two horizontal lines, with the cupcakes and doughnuts in lines one above the other. Establish that each child has an equal number of cupcakes and doughnuts. Place the plates side by side directly in front of the child.
4. Ask the children to put two cupcakes on a plate. Use the word *set* to describe the cupcakes. Describe a set as "a group of things that are alike." Doughnuts and cupcakes together do not make a set. A set may only be all doughnuts or all cupcakes. Then ask the children to make another set that has the same number of doughnuts as the first set on the empty plate. Give help freely as needed. When the second sets are completed, use the word *equal* to describe the two sets. Replace the cupcakes and doughnuts in their original positions in the lines. Repeat the procedure, asking the children to count out sets of additional numbers onto the first plate and then make equal sets on the second plate.
5. When the children have the idea, they can play with each other. One student can count out any number of cupcakes onto the first plate, and the second student can count and match the set. Or the teacher can write a big numeral on the board, and the children can count out matching sets for that numeral.
6. If you have already introduced the concepts *more than* and *less than* in your program, expand the game to include these concepts too.

Bakery Bonanza

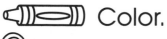  Color.

Cut.

Count and match. Paste.

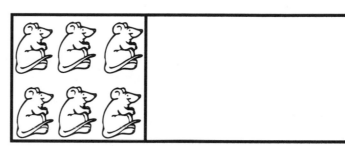

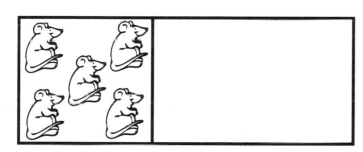

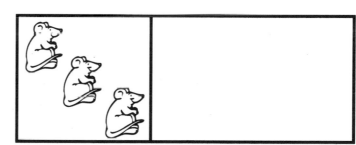

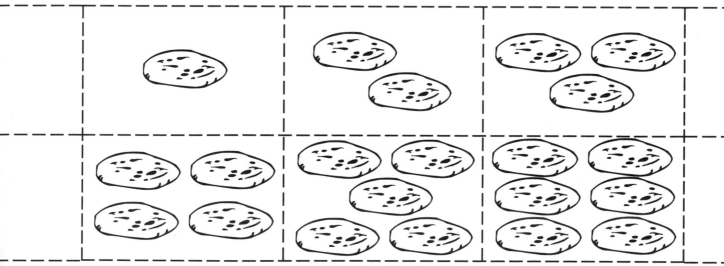

Name _____

Bake And Butter

 Color.

 Cut.

Count and match. Paste.

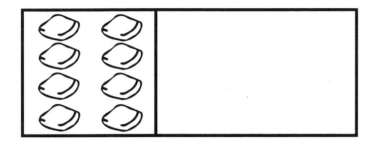

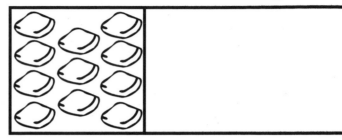

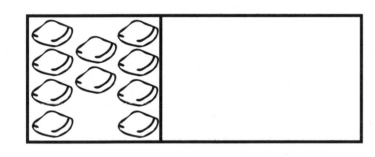

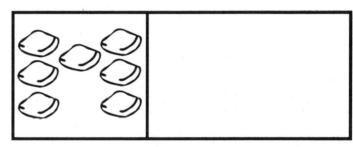

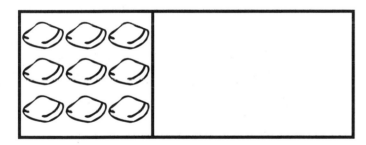

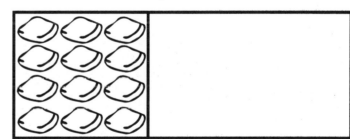

Beachcomber's Bucketful

Color the **equal** sets.

Hot Wheels Happy

Color the set that shows **more**.

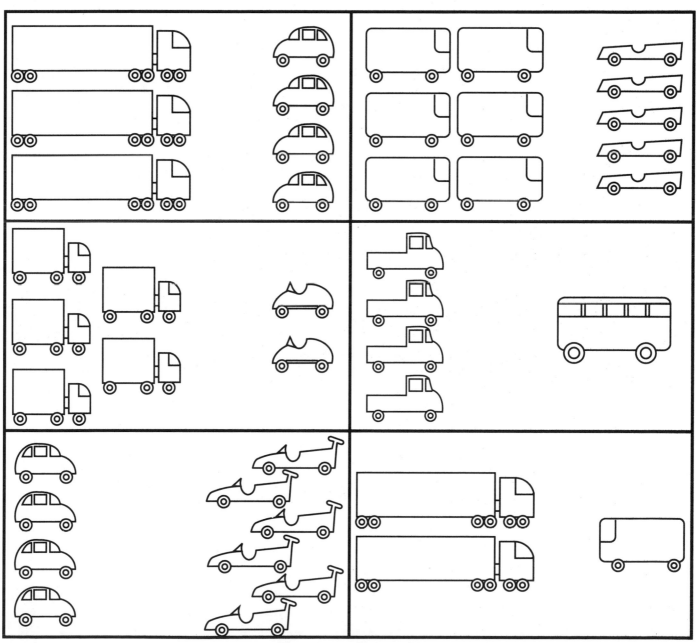

Lick 'n' Stick Pick

Color the set that shows **less**.

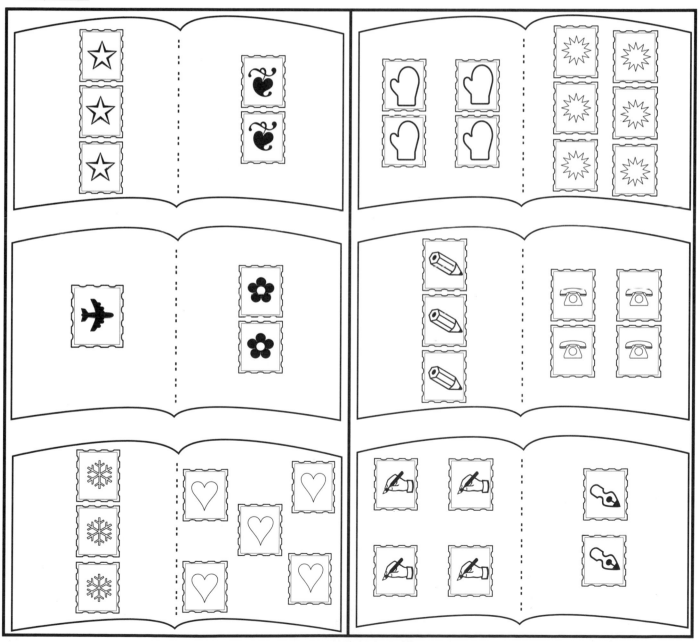

Collect The Butterflies

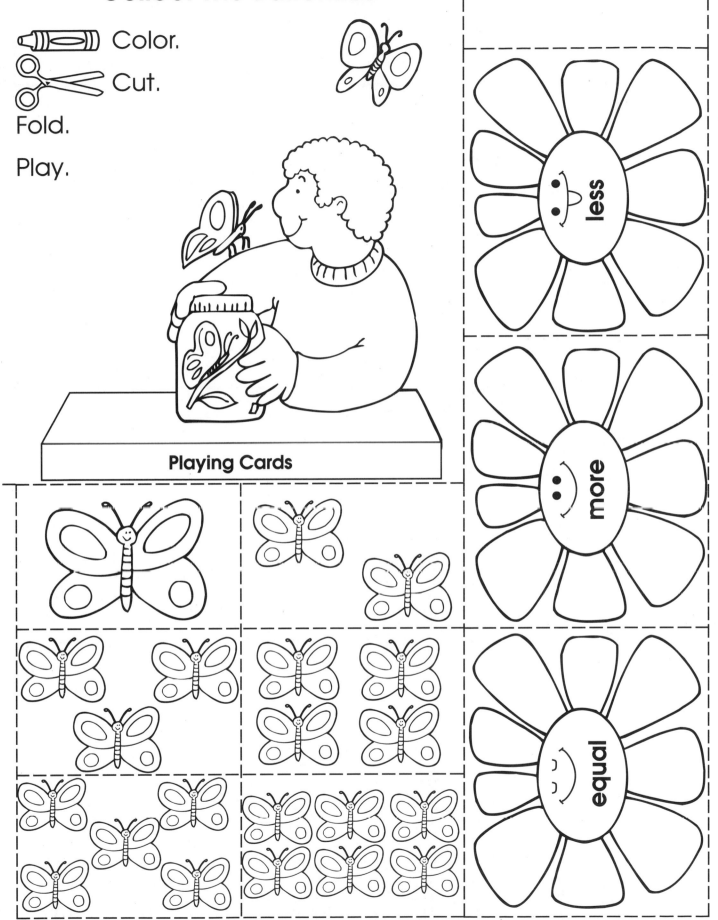

Color.

Cut.

Fold.

Play.

Playing Cards

less

more

equal

Use these with page 65.

Dear Parent,

We have been learning about important math words such as **equal**, **more**, and **less**. Understanding these terms will help your child as he or she learns beginning math concepts.

To play this game, your child will collect butterflies by making sets of butterflies that are equal to, more than, and less than a set shown on a playing card. To set up the game, lay the flowers with the words **equal, more,** and **less** in front of you. Turn the playing cards showing groups of butterflies facedown. Place the individual butterflies in a pile.

Mix up the butterfly playing cards and allow your child to pick one. Have your child: Count the number of butterflies pictured on the card. Find the **equal** flower. Put an **equal** number of the individual butterflies on that flower. Find the **more** flower. Put **more** butterflies on that flower than are on the set card. Find the **less** flower. Put **less** butterflies on that flower than are on the set card. If his or her answers are correct, he or she gets to keep the card, thus "collecting" the butterflies.

As an extension, make sets without the playing cards. Using the individual butterflies only, make a group of butterflies for your child. Make a group of less than six. Then your child can make another set that is equal to, more than, or less than the set you made. Switch roles and play again.

Have fun collecting those butterflies!

Treetoppers

Color the set that has **more**.

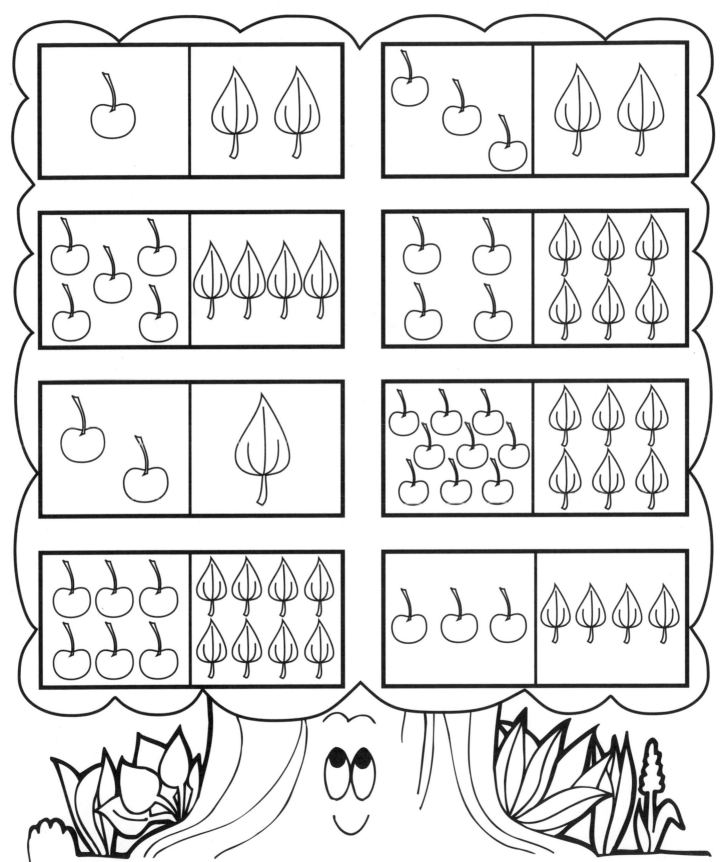

Additional Activity
Numbers And Number Words

Students will enjoy playing this fun game called Cherry-O. Duplicate a gameboard (page 70) and cherry markers (below) for each child and duplicate one set of number cards (pages 72 and 74) for you. Cut apart the markers and the number cards before beginning. To play, hold up a number card for all students to see. Then have each child place a cherry marker atop the matching number word on his gameboard. Check to see that all students have covered the correct number word.

Cherry Markers

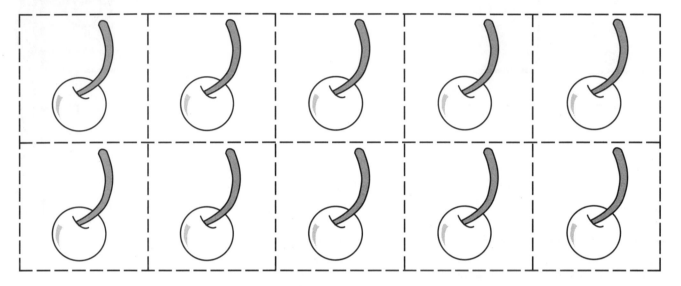

Cherry Chompers

Color the set that has **less**.

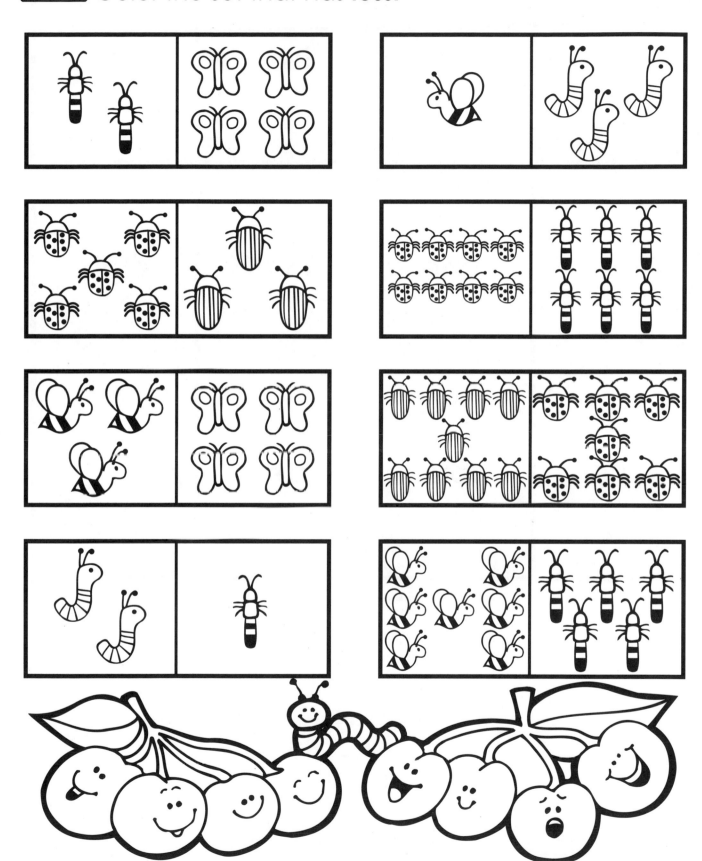

Gameboard

Use with "Numbers And Number Words" on page 68.

	six	two	nine
ten	one	five	eight
seven	four	three	

Cherry Orchard Count

Draw 🍒s.
Cut and paste the number words.

©The Education Center, Inc. • TEC880

one	two	three	four	five

Variation

For added fun and fine-motor practice, have youngsters punch holes in red construction paper. Instead of coloring cherries on each tree, have each child glue the right amount of construction-paper holes on each tree.

Number Cards

Use with "Numbers And Number Words" on page 68.

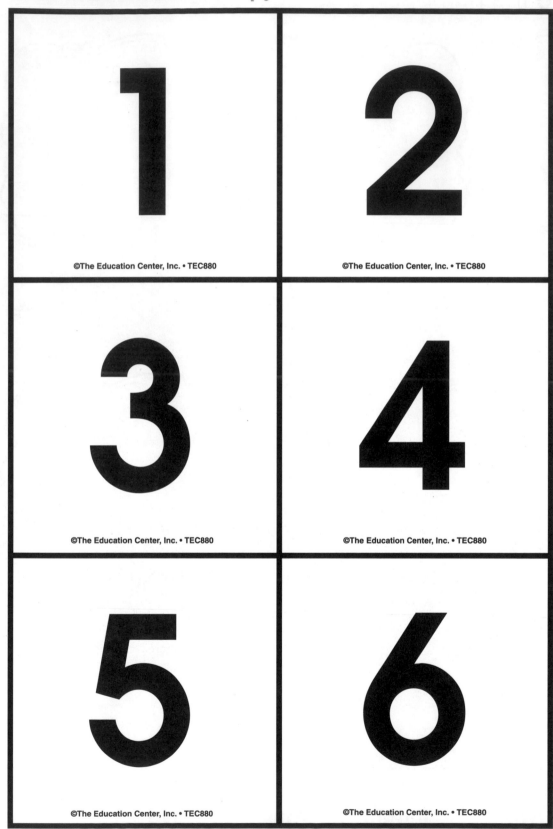

1

©The Education Center, Inc. • TEC880

2

©The Education Center, Inc. • TEC880

3

©The Education Center, Inc. • TEC880

4

©The Education Center, Inc. • TEC880

5

©The Education Center, Inc. • TEC880

6

©The Education Center, Inc. • TEC880

Name _____

Cherry Orchard Count

Draw 🍒s.
Cut and paste the number words.

| six | seven | eight | nine | ten |

Variation

For added fun and fine-motor practice, have youngsters punch holes in red construction paper. Instead of coloring cherries on each tree, have each child glue the right amount of construction-paper holes on each tree.

Number Cards

Use with "Numbers And Number Words" on page 68.

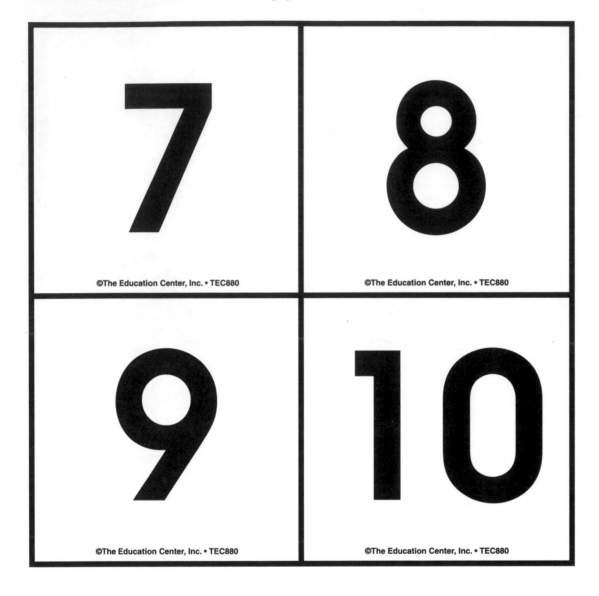

©The Education Center, Inc. • TEC880

©The Education Center, Inc. • TEC880

©The Education Center, Inc. • TEC880

©The Education Center, Inc. • TEC880

What comes next?

Color.

Cut. Paste.

Go Fish

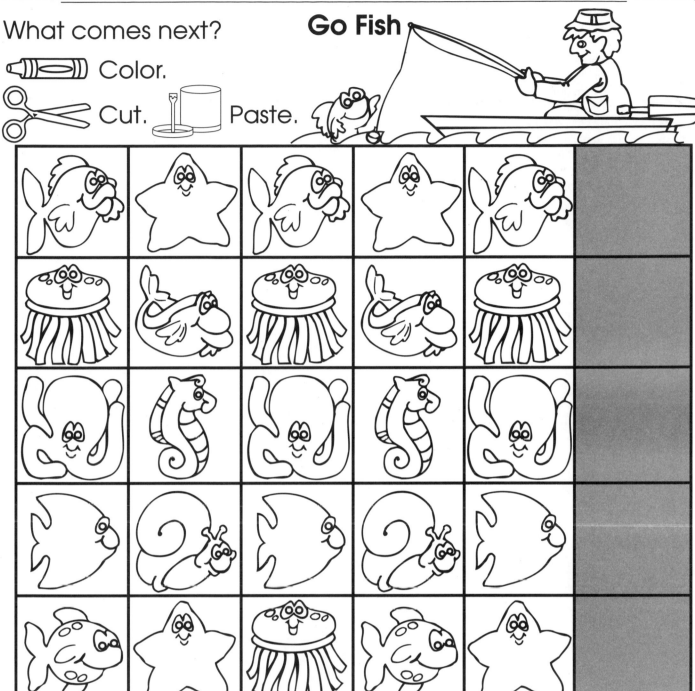

©The Education Center, Inc. • TEC880

Variation

For additional patterning practice, follow the directions below to make a learning center:

Enlarge and duplicate (several times) the pictures on the bottom of page 75 onto construction paper. Color the pictures, then laminate them and a large sheet of blue construction paper. (When choosing colors for each of the pictures, remember patterning considerations.) Cut apart the pictures on the dotted lines to make picture cards. Store all of the cards in a zippered bag; then place the bag of cards and the laminated blue sheet in a center. Have a child create patterns of his own by arranging the cards on the blue background.

Fish Find

Color.

Cut.

Paste.

Additional Activity
Fishy Pattern Mural

Create a fishy classroom mural with this patterning activity.
Cut a long one-foot-wide strip of blue bulletin-board paper.
(If desired, cut the paper to look like waves.) Mount the paper
to a wall. Then duplicate supplies of the fish cards below on
three different colors of construction paper and cut the cards
apart. Begin the activity by gluing the fish cards to the paper
in a simple pattern. Discuss the pattern with your students;
then allow students to glue additional cards to the paper to
continue the pattern.

Fish Cards

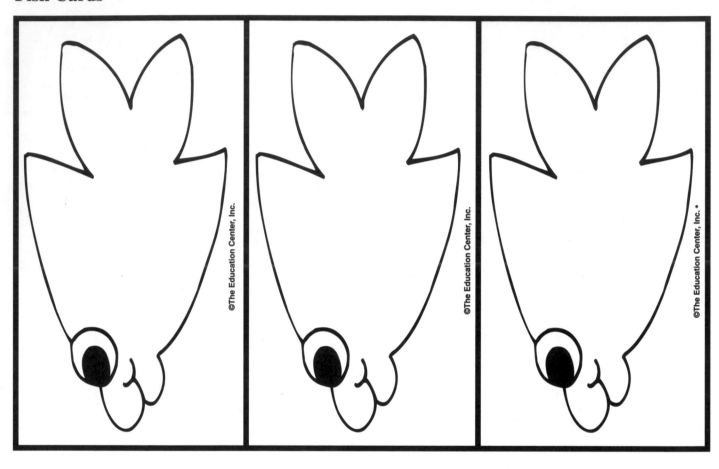

©The Education Center, Inc.

©The Education Center, Inc.

©The Education Center, Inc. •

Schools Of Fish

Read each numeral.
Color.

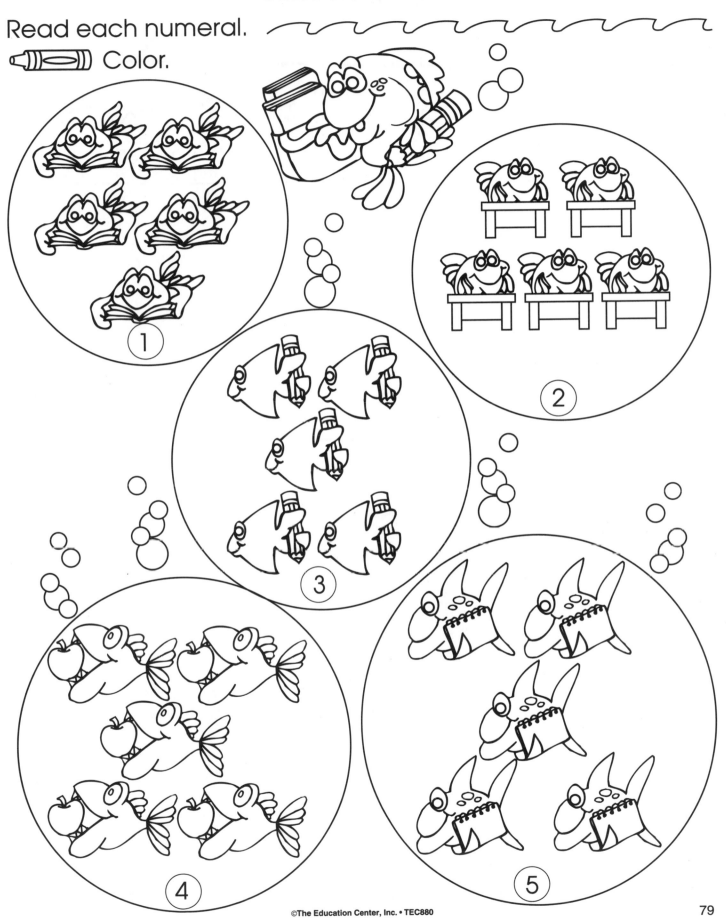

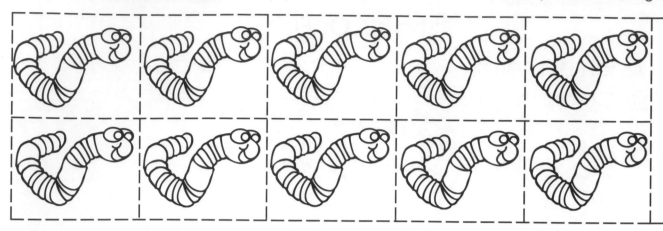

Dear Parent,

We have been fishing around with math skills at school! You and your child can have fun together at home while practicing counting and recognizing numerals.

To do this activity, have your child select a numeral card and place it in the shaded area on Felix's sign. Then have your child count out the corresponding number of worm cards and place them in the water, ready for Felix to eat.

For a variation of this activity, ask your child to place a given number of worms on the water. After he or she has correctly counted out the requested number of worm cards, have him or her find the corresponding numeral card to place in the shaded box on Felix's sign. By doing this activity, you are working on some very important math skills.

Have fun feeding Felix!

Feeding Felix

Color.

Cut.

Feed Felix.

1	2	3	4	5
6	7	8	9	10

How To Use Pages 80 And 81

1. For each student reproduce pages 80 and 81. Cut the parent note off the bottom of page 80. Have children color the worms on page 80 and the fish scene on page 81. Cut the worm and numeral cards apart on the dotted lines.

2. To do this activity, a child selects a numeral card and places it in the shaded box on Felix's sign. The child then counts and places the corresponding number of worm cards in the water, ready for Felix to eat.

3. As an alternate method of play, ask a child to place a given number of worm cards in the water. After he has correctly counted out the requested number of worm cards, have him find the corresponding numeral card to place in the shaded box on Felix's sign. This method can easily be played in cooperative team pairs.

4. Send the activity home in a zippered bag with the parent note on page 80 for continued practice.

Name _____

Mice Skating

✂ Cut.

Put the hockey pucks in order.

🧴 Glue.

🖍 Color.

1

Start

Finish

10

4	8	2	9	3	5	7	6

Starting Lineup

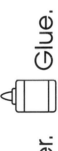 Cut.

Put the numerals in order. Glue.

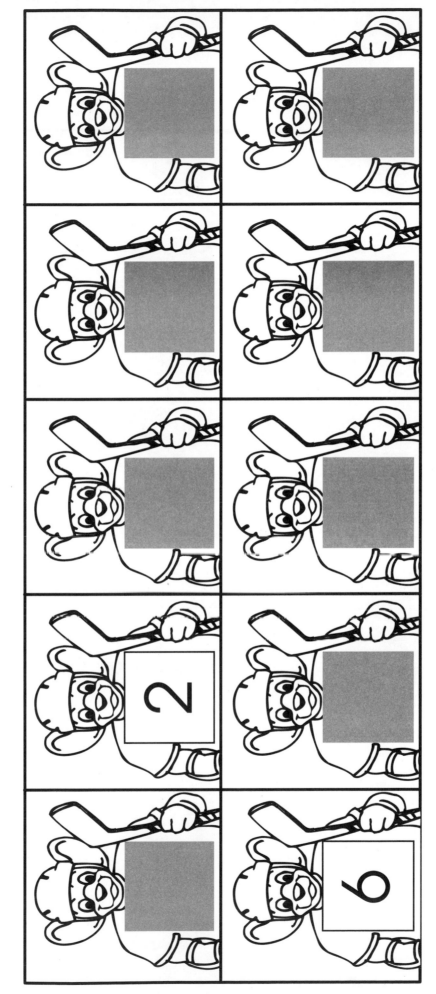

©The Education Center, Inc. • TEC880

"Go Goalie!"

How many pucks did the goalie stop?

Color to show how many.

The first one is done for you.

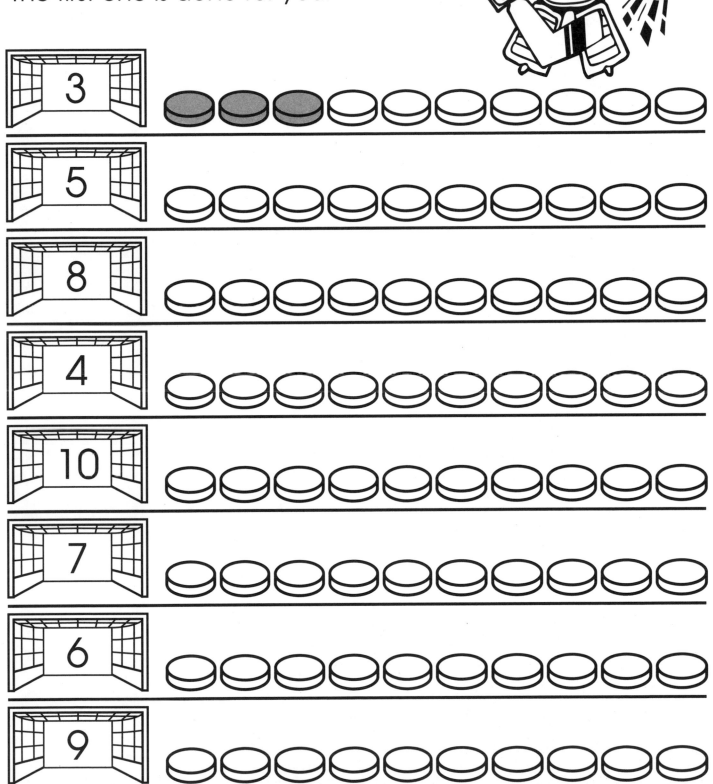

Hockey Hunt

Count.    Write.   Color.

SPORTING GOODS

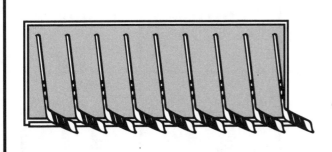

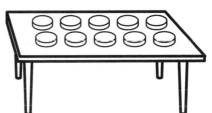
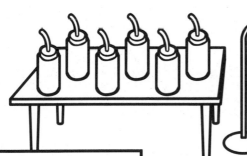
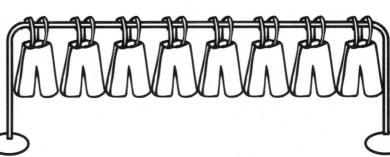

How many?

 _____

 _____

 _____

 _____

 _____

 _____

Patterns
Numeral Cards
Use with the hockey game on page 91.

1 ● one	**2** ●● two	**3** ●●● three	**4** ●●●● four	**5** ●●●●● five
6 ●●● ●●● six	**7** ●●●● ●●● seven	**8** ●●●● ●●●● eight	**9** ●●●●● ●●●● nine	**10** ●●●●● ●●●●● ten

fold

fold

Cut on the dotted lines.

fold

Glue
here.

fold

Glue
here.

How To Use Page 91

Make several hockey games for your children to share or help each child make his own. To make one hockey game, follow the directions listed below.

1. Duplicate the goal and numeral card patterns (pages 90 and 91) on construction paper.
2. Cut out the hockey goal along the bold outline; then cut on the dotted lines to form the opening in the net.
3. Fold the paper on each of the fold lines. (Be sure to fold the paper under, *away* from the printed page.)
4. Apply glue where it is indicated on the pattern.
5. Stand the goal on a table so that the net faces out. Balance the net by attaching the glued flaps to the portion of the pattern that is resting on the table (see illustration).
6. Cut apart the numeral cards; then laminate them if desired.
7. Provide a large supply of small manipulatives such as beans, buttons, or Styrofoam packing pieces that can be used as hockey pucks.
8. Send the goal, numeral cards, and a supply of hockey pucks home in a Ziploc® bag with the parent letter for continued counting practice at home.

How To Play The Game

Position the net on a table so there is a long, smooth, flat surface in front of the net. Secure the floor of the goal to the table with a piece of scotch tape. Place the numeral cards facedown in a deck near a bowl of manipulatives (hockey pucks). To play the game, a child draws a card from the deck, reads the numeral, then counts out that many pucks. For each puck, a child has three chances (adjust this number as necessary) to "hit" it into the goal. (A hit is done by flicking the index finger or middle finger off the thumb to shoot the hockey puck forward. Very young children may adapt their own methods of shooting the puck.) Each puck a child shoots into the goal may be kept in a personal pile. Play continues in the same manner with each additional player.

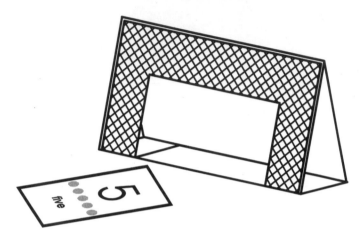

 Dear Parent,

We have been having fun counting and playing hockey at school! In this game you and your child can practice making number sets to ten. Tape the floor of the goal to a tabletop with a smooth surface. Place the numeral cards facedown on the table and the hockey pucks (counters) in a bowl. To play the game, your child turns over a numeral card, then counts out that many hockey pucks. For each puck in that set, your child has three chances to shoot the puck into the goal. (Your child will show you how this is done!) Each puck that your child shoots into the goal may be kept in a personal pile. Play continues in the same manner with each additional player.

You might even like to take a shot!

Use Your Noodle

 Cut.

Match the shapes.

 Paste.

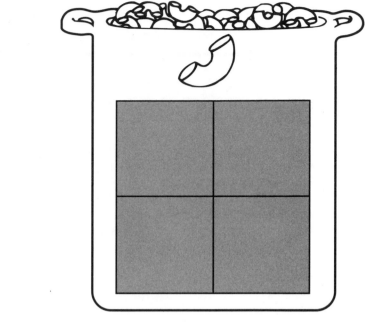

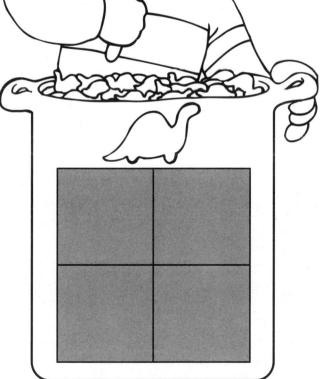

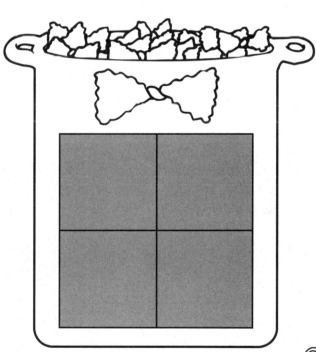

Variation

Cut off the illustrated pasta shapes at the bottom of the sheet before duplicating it. Provide real pasta shapes to be classified and glued instead of using the squares at the bottom of the sheet.

Extension Activities
Pasta Power/Math

— Provide a six-cup muffin tin and six assorted shapes of pasta. The children sort the shapes into the muffin cups.

— Provide a six-cup muffin tin and one type of pasta dyed six different colors. The children sort the pasta by color into the muffin cups.

— Provide a 12-cup muffin tin and 78 pieces of pasta. Number the muffin cups from 1 to 12. The children count out the pasta pieces into the corresponding muffin cups.

Name_____

Spoon Up The Pasta!

Cut.

Count the pasta.

Match. Paste.

Variation For Page 95

Cut off the pasta sets shown at the bottom of page 95 before duplicating it. Provide 15 real pasta pieces for each child. The children identify the numeral on each spoon handle and glue that many real pasta pieces onto the bowl of the spoon instead of pasting the squares at the bottom of the sheet.

Name _____

"Souper" Noodles

✂ Cut.

Count the pasta.

Match.

Paste.

	2	
1		3
4	5	

97

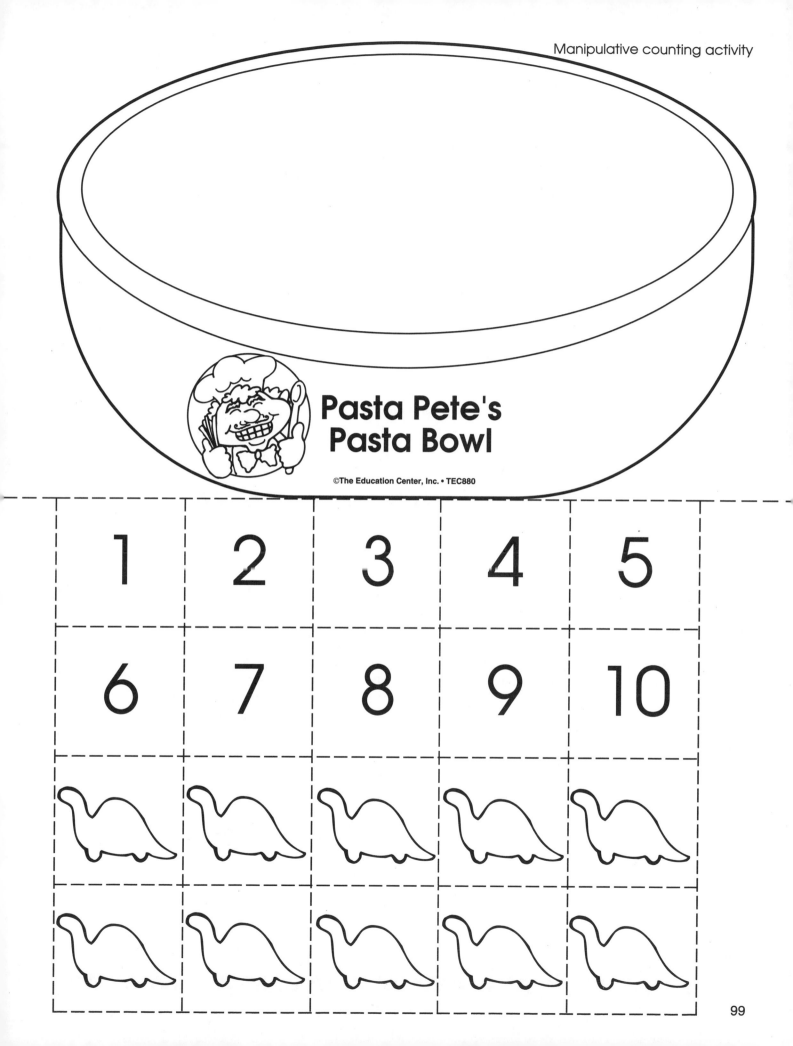

Pasta Pete's Pasta Bowl

©The Education Center, Inc. • TEC880

1	2	3	4	5
6	7	8	9	10

How To Use Page 99

1. Duplicate page 99 on construction paper for sturdiness.
2. Allow the children to color and cut out Pasta Pete's pasta bowl, the pasta shapes, and the numeral cards.
3. To play this manipulative counting game, the children count pasta shapes into Pasta Pete's bowl. For independent play, a child chooses a numeral card and counts that many pasta shapes into the bowl. You may also decide to give oral directions to guide the counting. If you are giving oral directions, try including directions that tell the children to construct sets of "more" and "less" than a particular numeral.
4. Send the game home in a Ziploc® bag with the parent note below for continued practice.

Variations

— Provide real pasta pieces for manipulative practice.

— Dye pasta pieces two colors for beginning addition practice. Try simple oral directions for addition. For example, say to the children, "Make a set of three red macaroni. Make a set of two green macaroni. How many do you have altogether? That's right, we say three plus two equals five." Help children make the sets on separate sides of the bowl to visually set up the math equation.

Dear Parent,

Play a pasta-counting game with Pasta Pete today. Your child has been learning about counting and numeral recognition at school. To play this game, turn the numeral cards face-down on a table. Allow your child to turn over a card and identify the numeral. Have your child count that many pasta shapes into Pasta Pete's bowl. Continue with all of the cards.

For an extra challenge, after your child has constructed a set for a numeral card, ask him or her to empty the bowl. Then ask your child to make a set with more pasta than he or she just had. Empty the bowl again and have your child make a set of pasta with less pieces. Understanding the concepts of more and less are important in beginning math skills.

If your child is ready, try some simple adding. Ask your child to make one set on the left side of the bowl. Ask him or her to make another set on the right side of the bowl. Ask how many he or she has altogether and repeat your child's answer using the whole addition equation. For example: "Make a set of three. Make a set of two. How many do you have altogether? That's right, we say three plus two equals five." Repeat this with several simple math sums.

Have plenty of fun with Pasta Pete!

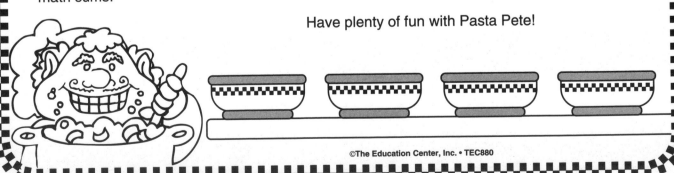

Fruit Fun

 Color.

Cut.

Play a counting game.

1	2	3	4	5
6	7	8	9	10

How To Use Pages 101 and 103

1. Reproduce pages 101 and 103 for each child. Cut the parent note off the bottom of page 103. Allow the children to color the berries on page 103 and the toucan and leaf on page 101. Cut the berries and numeral cards apart on the dotted lines.

2. To play the game, the children select a numeral card and place it in the shaded box on the toucan's body. The children then place the corresponding number of berries onto the leaf, ready to feed to the toucan.

3. As an alternate method of play, ask the children to place a given number of berries on the leaf. After they have correctly counted out the requested number of berries, the children should find the corresponding numeral card to place in the shaded box on the toucan. This method can easily be played in cooperative team pairs.

4. Send home the game and numeral and berry pieces with the parent note on page 103 in a Ziploc® bag for continued practice at home.

Background For The Teacher
Toucans

No clown ever had a nose as big and funny as the toucan! Actually, nobody knows why its bill is so big, but it can grow to one-third of the bird's body length! The most familiar toucan is the Toco toucan, with its black body, big colorful bill, and white feathers around the throat like a bib.

Toucans live mainly in the warm rain forests of Central and South America, although some species live in the Andes mountains. Little is understood about the everyday life of many species of toucans. They spend their lives high above the forest floor, preening each other with their great bills, raising their babies, eating fruit, and drinking and bathing in pools of water that collect in the hallows of branches. Sometimes toucans use their bills to play a game of catch with a piece of fruit, tossing it back and forth like a ball. The bill is also a big help when a toucan tries to reach a juicy piece of fruit far out on a limb. A toucan picks the fruit with the tip of its bill, then tosses it up and catches it in the back of its mouth with a snap. Some people think that the big bill frightens smaller birds. Because each toucan's bill is a slightly different size, color, and pattern, it might be a way for toucans to identify each other. Sometimes toucans grab each others' bill and wrestle until one gives up. Observers say it is more like a game than a fight.

Toucans lay eggs in holes in the trunks of trees. The parents do not make the holes, but find abandoned holes or drive out woodpeckers. They take turns sitting on the eggs for about an hour. The babies, born blind and featherless, have small bills with dull colors. As they grow, their bills become large and brightly colored. Some species of toucans are becoming rarer as their rain forest homes are cut down for farms, and one species is currently listed as threatened.

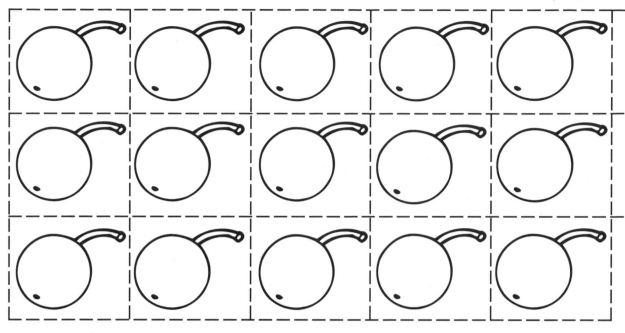

Dear Parent,

We have been practicing our counting skills at school with the help of a colorful toucan! You can help your child by playing a counting game called Fruit Fun.

To play this game, put the playing board with the toucan and his leaf in front of your child. Spread the numeral cards, faceup and out of order, to one side of the board. Spread out the fruit counting cards on the other side of the board.

Say a number for your child, and ask him or her to find that numeral card and place it in the shaded box on the toucan's body. Then ask your child to count that many fruits by placing the correct number of fruit cards on the large leaf.

For an extra challenge, after a numeral card has been placed in the box on the toucan, ask your child to put one more fruit than the numeral shown on the card on the leaf. Try two more or three more. Do the same thing by having your child put one less (or two less or three less) fruit(s) on the leaf.

These counting and more and less concepts are crucial for beginning math skills. You are playing a vital role in helping your child master important skills.

Have fruit fun with counting!

Additional Activity
Counting Toucans

Here's an activity that helps students practice their counting skills. Duplicate student copies of the toucan below. Then duplicate the bowl patterns on page 106 so that each child has ten bowls. Have each child color her toucan and number her bowls from one to ten; then have her cut out the bowls and the toucan. Next have the child glue the toucan to the center of a large sheet of construction paper. Have her glue the bowls to the construction paper around the toucan. To begin the counting activity, give each child a pile of colored ring-shaped cereal. Have the child glue the correct number of cereal pieces to each bowl. Be sure to provide extra cereal for snacking!

Toucan Pattern

©The Education Center, Inc. • TEC880

Jungle Fruits

Read the numeral.
Draw the fruit.

Variation

Instead of having children draw fruit on the trees, provide ring-shaped fruit-flavored cereal for the children to count and glue on the trees.

Bowl Patterns

Use with "Counting Toucans" on page 104.

©The Education Center, Inc.

Toucan Treats

Cut.
Match.
Paste.

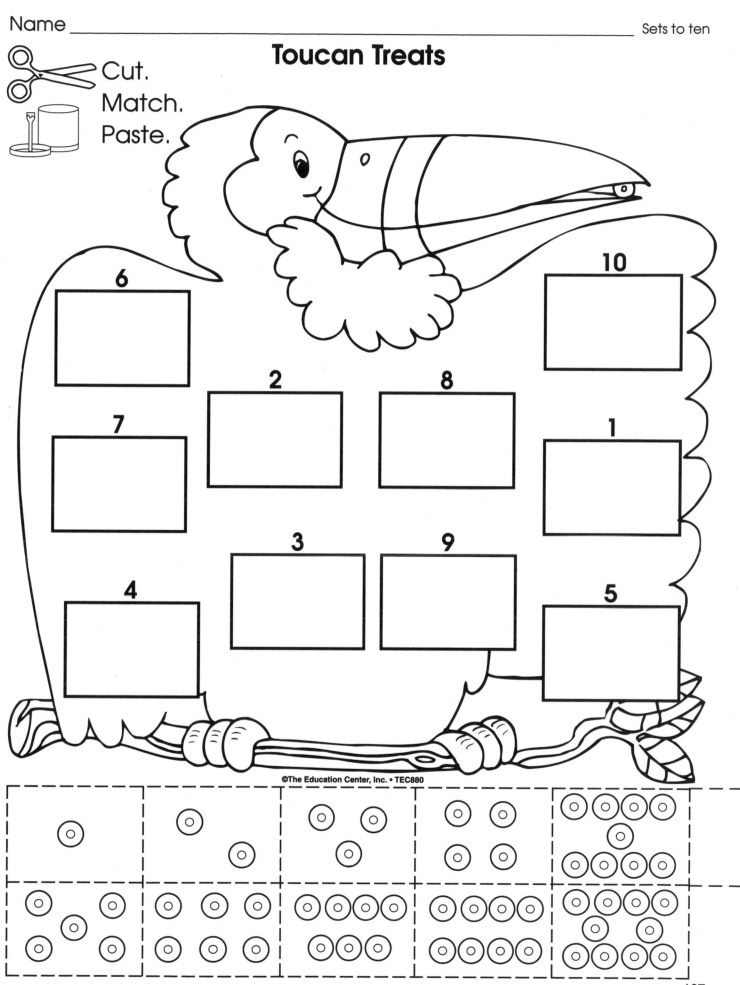

©The Education Center, Inc. • TEC880

Where's My Mama?

 Draw lines to match.

 five

 two

 three

 four

 one

There are _____ sheep in the flock.

Bonus Box: Color the lambs and ewes yellow if their numbers are bigger than two.

Pattern

Use the pattern below to make number word and number set/numeral matching cards for extra practice in recognizing number words.

©The Education Center, Inc. • TEC880

Reward

Use the reward below to recognize progress in reading number words.

Good For "Ewe"!

_____
child's name

has learned to read number words!

_____   _____
teacher   date

©The Education Center, Inc. • TEC880

Name _____

Frisky Frolic

Help the shepherd check his flock.

✏️ Draw a red line to show his path.

one · two · three · four · five · six · seven · eight · nine · ten

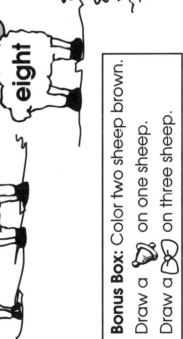

Bonus Box: Color two sheep brown.
Draw a 🔔 on one sheep.
Draw a 🎀 on three sheep.

Buzzzzz!

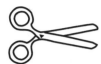 Cut. Paste.

five

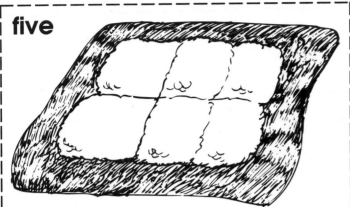

The fleece is tied up and ready to sell.

two

The shearer holds a sheep on its back.

one

It is spring. The woolly sheep are too hot!

four

The wool comes off in one piece. Now it is called fleece.

six

Cool at last!

three

"Buzzzzz!" go the clippers.

How To Use Page 113

1. Provide a 6" x 18" piece of construction paper for each child.
2. Allow the children to color and cut out the picture squares.
3. The children read the number words in the picture squares and paste the squares to the construction-paper strip in number order from top to bottom to tell the story of how a sheep is sheared.

Variation

Instead of pasting the picture squares to the construction paper, simply stack them in order from top to bottom and staple in the upper left corner to make a booklet.

Background For The Teacher
Sheep

Sheep are very important to people. They give us food (lamb and mutton) and materials (wool and leather). In a flock of sheep, there are *ewes* (females), *rams* (males), and *lambs* (babies). The horns of most rams curl outward. In some breeds, both rams and ewes have horns. In others, only rams have horns. In still others, neither rams nor ewes have horns. There are numerous breeds of sheep, each bred for its various grades of wool or for its meat.

Sheep are relatively easy to raise, and they can be found all over the world. They need little water and will eat grass, weeds, shrubs, grain, or hay. They do need large ranges of land to graze. A large herd of sheep in the United States can have as many as 2,000 or more sheep. Smaller flocks of less than 100 sheep can also be found on smaller farms. Sheep within a flock can identify their families by a scent given off by a special sac found between the two toes of their hooves.

During the winter months, sheep grow a heavy coat of wool. In the spring, the shearer uses electric clippers to remove the coat. A large canvas is spread on the ground and one sheep at a time is sheared. The wool is removed in one piece. When it is off the sheep, it is called *fleece*. The outside is dirty, matted, and full of weeds, but the underside is clean and soft. Depending upon the breed, wool can be white, pale yellow, gray, brown, or black. It takes about ten minutes to shear a sheep. The fleece is folded into a bundle, with the clean, inner side out, and tied with a special twine made out of paper. This twine won't shed fibers onto the fleece. It can then be shipped to market.

Name_____

Leaping Lulu

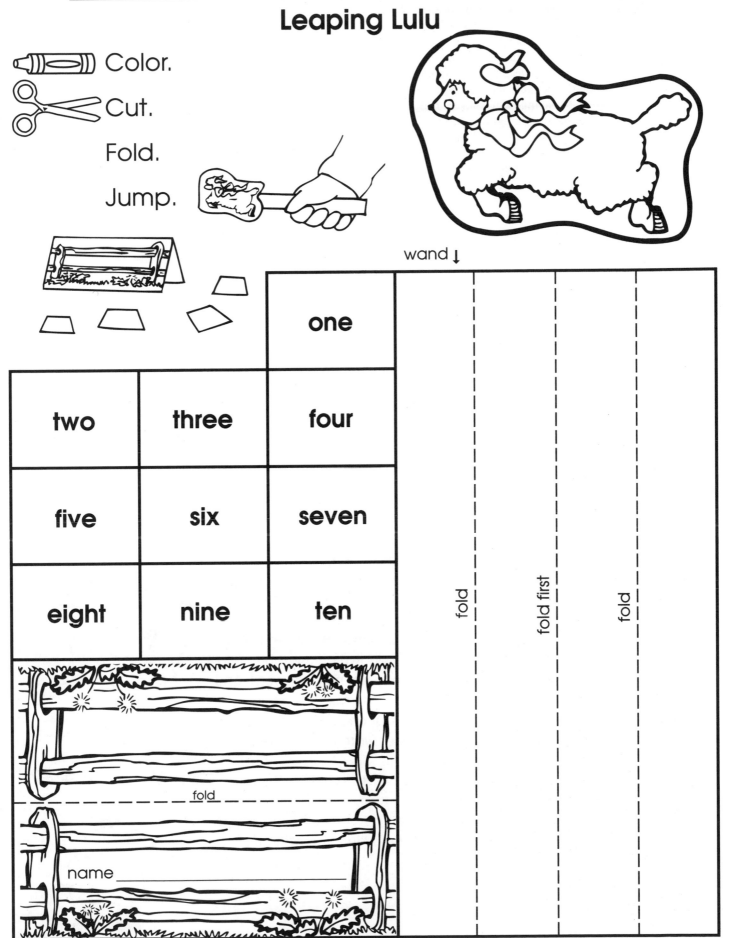

Color.

Cut.

Fold.

Jump.

wand ↓

		one
two	three	four
five	six	seven
eight	nine	ten

fold

fold first

fold

fold

name_____

How To Use Page 115

1. Duplicate one sheet on construction paper for each child.
2. Color and cut out the pieces on the solid lines.
3. Fold the wand in half twice (not accordion-style). Staple the lamb to the tip as shown in the illustration on the worksheet. **Note:** For left-handed children, staple the lamb to the opposite tip. Fold the fence so it stands up.
4. Tell your children that Leaping Lulu is a very happy lamb. She spends her days jumping over pasture fences with other lambs. We will play a game to help Lulu jump. Begin by turning the number word cards face-down. Turn over one card. Read the number. Make Lulu jump over the fence that many times. If you are correct, you may keep the card. If not, return the card to the table facedown. Repeat until you have all the cards.
5. Send the game home in a Ziploc® bag with the note below for continued learning.

Dear Parent,

Leaping Lulu! What a jumping game your child has to play today! Leaping Lulu is a happy lamb that loves to jump over her fence, but she will only jump if your child correctly reads the number words. So let's leap right in and play.

Make sure Lulu is still attached to her handle, and fold her fence so it will stand up. Lay the number word cards facedown on the table. Allow your child to turn over a number word card, read the number word, and make Lulu jump that many times over the fence. If your child is correct, he or she keeps the card. If not, your child puts it back on the table facedown. Continue playing until all the number word cards have been read.

For an extra challenge, add more number words to help build your child's vocabulary.

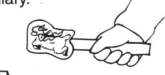

Happy leaping with Lulu!

Name _____

Real Blackberry Fun

Write how many in the set.
Add.

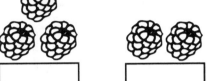

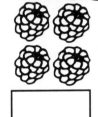

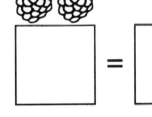
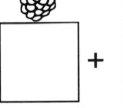

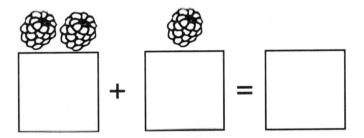
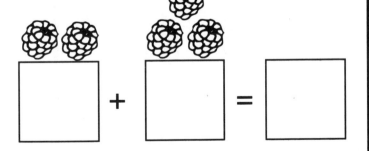

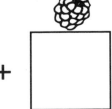

☐	+	☐	=	☐		☐	+	☐	=	☐
☐	+	☐	=	☐		☐	+	☐	=	☐
☐	+	☐	=	☐		☐	+	☐	=	☐
☐	+	☐	=	☐		☐	+	☐	=	☐

Extension Activity
Berry Addition

Duplicate four copies of the berry cards below for each pair of students. Cut out the cards. To play, students stack the cards facedown. In turn, one player turns over two cards from the stack. Then he adds to determine the total number of berries on the two cards. If he is correct, he keeps the cards. If he is incorrect, he returns the cards to the bottom of the stack. Play continues in this manner until the stack of cards is diminished.

Berry Cards

Name _____

Delicious Blackberries

Write how many in each set. Add.

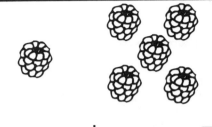
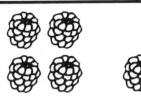

_____ + _____ = _____   _____ + _____ = _____

_____ + _____ = _____   _____ + _____ = _____

_____ + _____ = _____   _____ + _____ = _____

_____ + _____ = _____   _____ + _____ = _____

_____ + _____ = _____   _____ + _____ = _____

Extension Activity
Berry Baskets

Duplicate a set of berry baskets (below) for each child. Have students cut out their baskets and position the cutouts in front of them. To begin, ask each child to identify a basket with a certain number of berries in it. When the child finds this basket, ask him to color a certain number of additional berries in the basket. Then have the child add the berries together to determine the total. Continue in this manner until all of the baskets have been used.

Berry Baskets

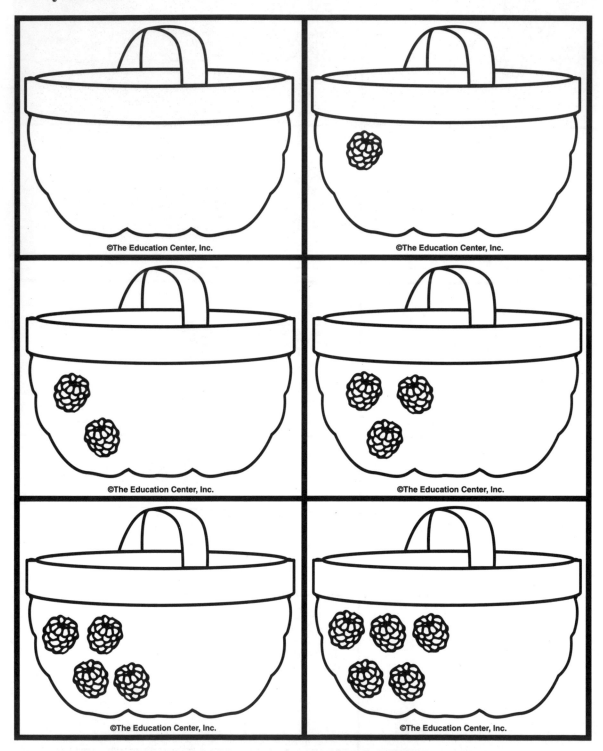

©The Education Center, Inc.

Name _____

Baskets Of Berries

Cut out berries.
Use as counters to solve each problem.
Write answers.

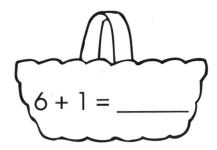 0 + 5 = _____

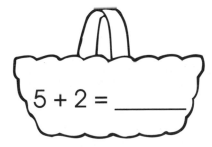 5 + 1 = _____

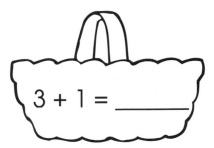 2 + 5 = _____

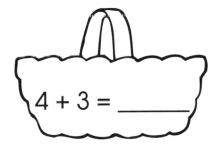 6 + 1 = _____

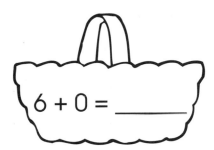 6 + 0 = _____

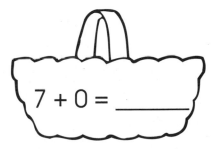 3 + 1 = _____

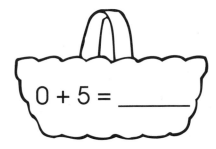 4 + 3 = _____

5 + 2 = _____

7 + 0 = _____

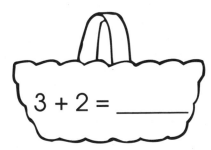 3 + 2 = _____

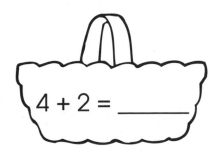 4 + 2 = _____

 1 + 6 = _____

121

Bunches Of Berries

Cut and add.

How To Use Page 123

1. Duplicate page 123 for each child.
2. Allow the children to cut the blackberries off the bottom of the sheet.
3. To use this manipulative sheet, the children form a set of berries on each side of the plus sign on the basket. The children should add the sets together to get the sum.
4. Remove the berries, create more sets, and add to find their sums.

Name _____

Butterfly Buddies

Add.
Color by the code.

7—yellow   5—red   4—purple
6—orange   3—green

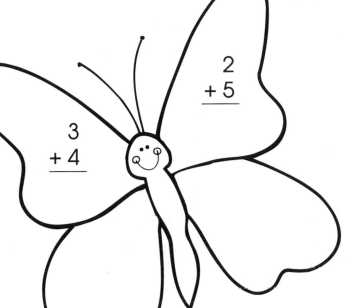

$$\begin{array}{r} 2 \\ +5 \\ \hline \end{array}$$

$$\begin{array}{r} 3 \\ +4 \\ \hline \end{array}$$

$$\begin{array}{r} 2 \\ +4 \\ \hline \end{array}$$

$$\begin{array}{r} 3 \\ +3 \\ \hline \end{array}$$

$$\begin{array}{r} 4 \\ +0 \\ \hline \end{array}$$

$$\begin{array}{r} 2 \\ +2 \\ \hline \end{array}$$

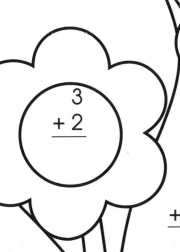

$$\begin{array}{r} 3 \\ +2 \\ \hline \end{array}$$

$$\begin{array}{r} 2 \\ +1 \\ \hline \end{array}$$

$$\begin{array}{r} 4 \\ +1 \\ \hline \end{array}$$

$$\begin{array}{r} 3 \\ +0 \\ \hline \end{array}$$

Bonus Box: Write a story about
butterfly friends on the back.

Extension Activities
Butterflies/Addition Facts

— Reproduce ten butterflies using the pattern below. Number each butterfly with a different number for the sums you want your children to work on. Duplicate circles the size of the circles on the butterfly for each addition fact. Laminate and cut out all the pieces. The children practice their facts by choosing a circle with an addition fact, solving the fact, and placing it on the corresponding butterfly.

— Reduce the pattern below so 12 butterflies fit on a regular sheet of copy paper. Duplicate one copy of the 12 butterflies for each child. The children may cut out the butterflies and use them as counters to help solve the addition facts in this unit.

— Reproduce the pattern below for butterfly flash cards for extra practice and drill with addition facts. Duplicate enough butterflies for each addition fact the children need to work on. Write the addition facts on the fronts of the butterflies and the sums on the backs. Children may drill each other in their free time, or you may choose to hold a "Butterfly Math Facts Bee," similar to a spelling bee!

126

Butterfly Sets

 Write how many in the set.
 Add.

$$+\ 2$$

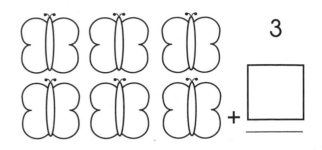
$$3$$
$$+\ \boxed{}$$

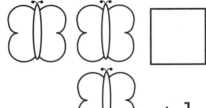
$$+\ 1$$

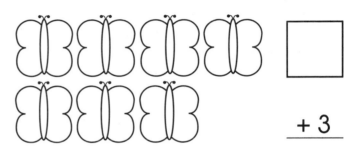
$$+\ 3$$

$$2$$
$$+\ \boxed{}$$

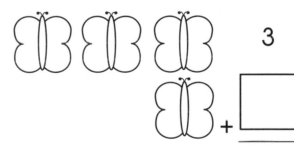
$$3$$
$$+\ \boxed{}$$

$$+\ 0$$

Bonus Box: Draw two sets of butterflies and write an addition fact.

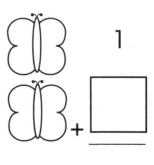
$$1$$
$$+\ \boxed{}$$

Flying Facts

Cut out the circle ⭕.
Paste on the butterfly 🦋.

10

9

8

5 + 5

5 + 3

8 + 1

6 + 4

4 + 4

7 + 2

Butterfly Beginnings

Draw a line to match the butterfly and the caterpillar.

Bonus Box: Draw your favorite butterfly on the back.

Name _____

Flutter-By Facts

 Cut.

Match.

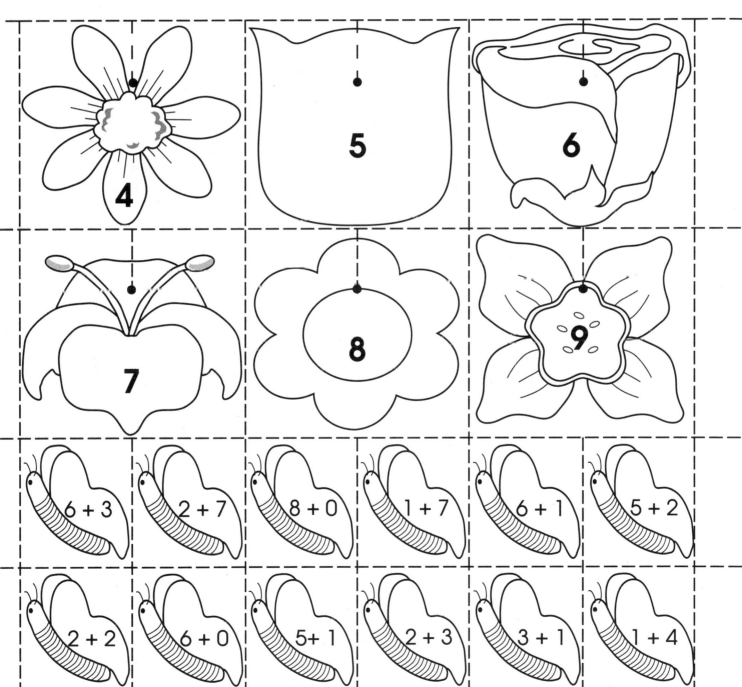

4

5

6

7

8

9

| 6 + 3 | 2 + 7 | 8 + 0 | 1 + 7 | 6 + 1 | 5 + 2 |

| 2 + 2 | 6 + 0 | 5 + 1 | 2 + 3 | 3 + 1 | 1 + 4 |

How To Use Page 113

1. Duplicate page 113 on construction paper for sturdiness.
2. Allow the children to color the butterflies and flowers **lightly** so the facts and sums will not be covered by coloring.
3. Allow the children to cut out the butterflies and flowers on the dotted lines, forming squares around all the pieces for easy cutting.
4. Help the children cut to the center of each flower by cutting only on the dotted lines on each flower. If desired, reinforce each flower with tape over the dotted lines before cutting.
5. To play, the children solve the fact on each butterfly and insert the butterfly in the cut on the flower with the corresponding sum so the butterfly looks as if it has landed in the flower. (See the worksheet for an illustration.)
6. Send home the flowers and butterflies with the parent note below for continued learning.

Variation

If you prefer not using this sheet as a game, provide a sheet of manila paper with each worksheet. Allow the children to cut out all the pieces. Have the children glue the flowers along the bottom, long edge of the manila paper in numerical order. As each fact on the butterflies is solved, the children may glue the butterflies above the corresponding flower.

Dear Parent,

Have some butterfly fun with fluttery facts! Your child has been practicing his math addition facts at school. In this game, your child needs to help the butterflies find their flower home by solving basic addition facts.

Each flower has been slit to hold the butterflies. To play, place all the butterflies and flowers on the table. Allow your child to choose a butterfly, solve the problem, and match it to the flower with the corresponding sum by inserting the butterfly in the slit in the flower. Each flower will have two butterflies in it by the end of the game.

For an extra challenge, help your child begin to see that several facts have the same sum. Ask your child to find all the butterflies with the sum of five (or six, or seven, etc.). When all the facts for that sum have been found, choose another sum to work with. This will help your child begin to see relationships in math facts!

Enjoy your flutter-facts!

Name _____

Dragon Flower

Write how many in the set.
Add.

[ ] + [ ] = [ ]   [ ] + [ ] = [ ]

[ ] + [ ] = [ ]   [ ] + [ ] = [ ]

[ ] + [ ] = [ ]   [ ] + [ ] = [ ]

[ ] + [ ] = [ ]   [ ] + [ ] = [ ]

Pattern

Use the pattern below to make flash cards to practice math facts.

©The Education Center, Inc. • TEC880

Reward

Send the reward home to recognize achievement in math facts.

Hot Dog!

_____
child's name

has made
great progress
in math facts.

_____   _____
teacher   date

©The Education Center, Inc. • TEC880

Name

All In The Family

Cut.

Paste.

5

4

3

2 + 3	2 + 1	0 + 3	4 + 1	2 + 2	3 + 1

Extension Activity
Acting Out Addition

Your students will enjoy practicing their addition skills with this dramatic activity. Designate students to act out characters such as dragons, flowers, and castles. Dictate a story problem using these characters and have students act them out and then solve the problems. Here are a few sample story problems:

Three dragons are standing outside the castle.
(Three students pretend to be dragons and one student pretends to be a castle.)
Two more dragons came along to join them.
(Two more students pretend to be dragons.)
How many dragons are standing outside the castle?

A dragon picked two flowers.
(One student pretends to be a dragon and two students pretend to be flowers.)
Another dragon picked four flowers.
(Another student pretends to be a dragon and four more students pretend to be flowers.)
How many flowers did they pick altogether?

Marshmallow Roast

Write how many in the set. Add.

🍥🍥 + 🍥🍥🍥 ___ + ___ = ___	🍥🍥 + 🍥🍥🍥🍥🍥 ___ + ___ = ___
🍥🍥🍥 + 🍥🍥🍥🍥 ___ + ___ = ___	🍥🍥🍥 + 🍥 ___ + ___ = ___
🍥🍥🍥🍥 + 🍥 ___ + ___ = ___	🍥🍥 + 🍥🍥🍥🍥 ___ + ___ = ___
🍥🍥🍥 + 🍥🍥🍥 ___ + ___ = ___	🍥🍥 + 🍥🍥 ___ + ___ = ___
🍥🍥🍥🍥🍥🍥 + 🍥 ___ + ___ = ___	🍥🍥🍥🍥🍥 + 🍥 ___ + ___ = ___

Dragon Delight

Add.

Color by the code.

7—**red**   5—**brown**   3—**purple**
6—**yellow**   4—**green**

Castle Calculations

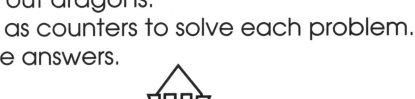

Cut out dragons.
Use as counters to solve each problem.
Write answers.

3 + 1 =

1 + 4 =

3 + 5 =

5 + 2 =

2 + 8 =

1 + 5 =

4 + 5 =

6 + 4 =

©The Education Center, Inc. • TEC880

Snazzy Snake

Add.

 Write.

2 + 2 =

2 + 0 =

3 + 1 =

3 + 2 =

2 + 1 =

5 + 0 =

1 + 3 =

How To Use Pages 145 And 146

1. Duplicate page 145 and the snake counters below for each child.
2. Have each child color the snake counters, then cut them apart.
3. Direct each child to use the snake counters to determine the sums; then write the correct numerals in the spaces provided.

Patterns
Snake Counters
Use with "Snazzy Snake" on page 145.

Name _____

Yummy Seeds

Count how many seeds in each set.
Write.
Add.

_____ + _____ = _____

_____ + _____ = _____

_____ + _____ = _____

_____ + _____ = _____

_____ + _____ = _____

_____ + _____ = _____

_____ + _____ = _____

_____ + _____ = _____

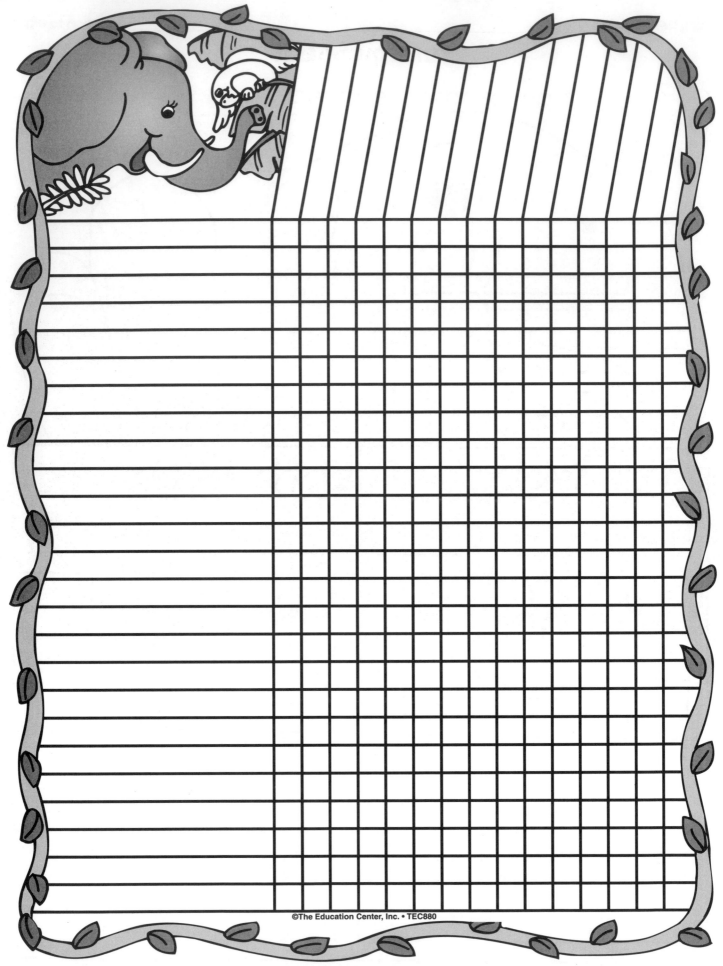

©The Education Center, Inc. • TEC880

Note To The Teacher: Photocopy the page. List your students' names in the left column. Record the desired skills, activities, or events in the spaces at the top of the grid. Keep this grid handy for record keeping.

Name 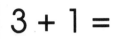 _____

Jungle Pals

Add.
Write the answer.

3 + 1 =

2 + 5 =

4 + 4 =

2 + 2 =

4 + 2 =

3 + 5 =

1 + 7 =

3 + 0 =

Parent Note

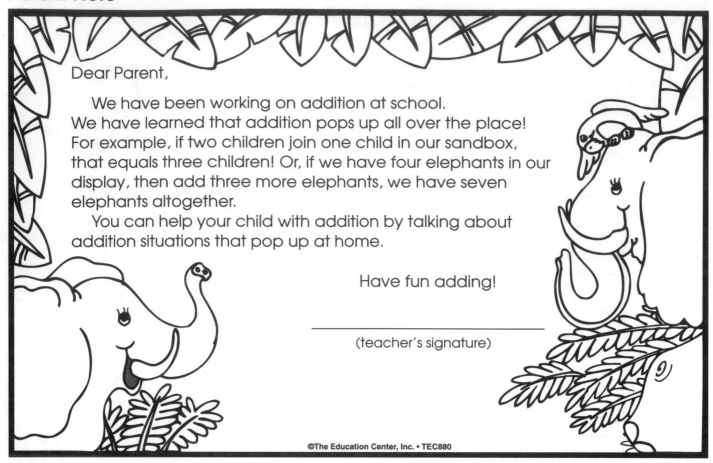

Dear Parent,

We have been working on addition at school.
We have learned that addition pops up all over the place!
For example, if two children join one child in our sandbox,
that equals three children! Or, if we have four elephants in our
display, then add three more elephants, we have seven
elephants altogether.

You can help your child with addition by talking about
addition situations that pop up at home.

Have fun adding!

_____
(teacher's signature)

Award

_____ is swinging
(name)

right along with addition!

_____
(teacher's signature)

Note To The Teacher: For each child, photocopy an award/note (pages 150 and 152) as it applies.

Name _____

Leaves For Lunch

Cut out the leaves for counters.
Add.
Write.

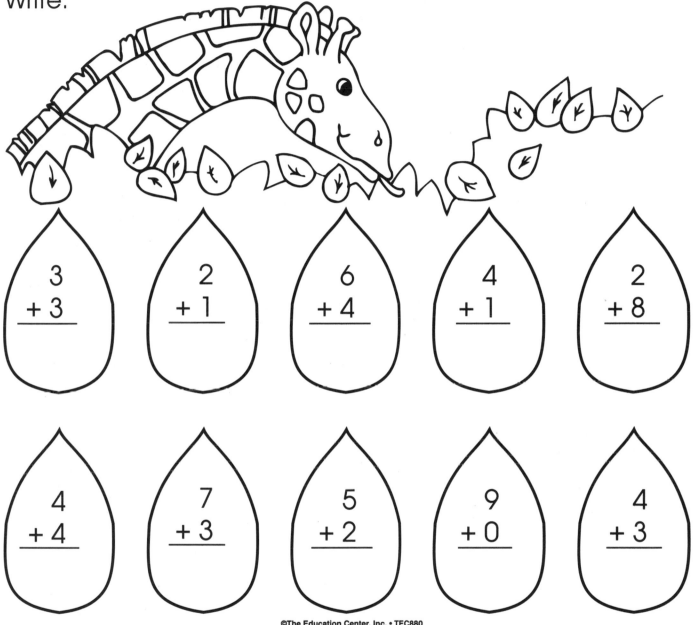

$\begin{array}{r} 3 \\ +3 \\ \hline \end{array}$
$\begin{array}{r} 2 \\ +1 \\ \hline \end{array}$
$\begin{array}{r} 6 \\ +4 \\ \hline \end{array}$
$\begin{array}{r} 4 \\ +1 \\ \hline \end{array}$
$\begin{array}{r} 2 \\ +8 \\ \hline \end{array}$

$\begin{array}{r} 4 \\ +4 \\ \hline \end{array}$
$\begin{array}{r} 7 \\ +3 \\ \hline \end{array}$
$\begin{array}{r} 5 \\ +2 \\ \hline \end{array}$
$\begin{array}{r} 9 \\ +0 \\ \hline \end{array}$
$\begin{array}{r} 4 \\ +3 \\ \hline \end{array}$

How To Use The Note Below

1. Photocopy the note below as needed; then cut it out.
2. Fill in the child's name and some addition facts that child needs to practice such as "Addition facts to 12."
3. Send the note home with the child.

Parent Note

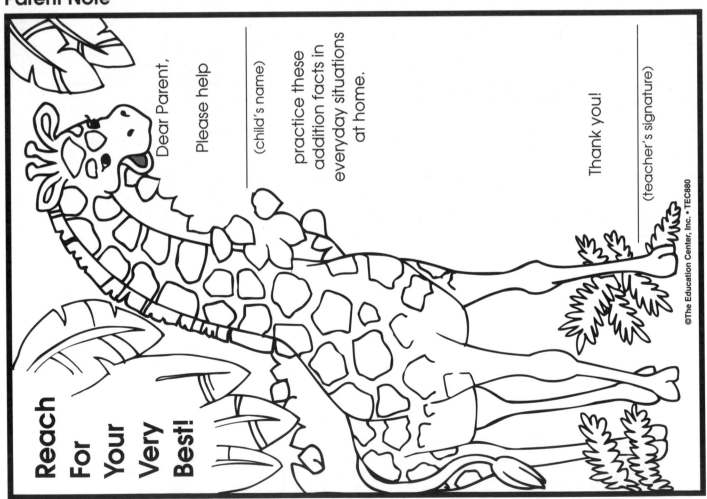

Dear Parent,

Please help _____ (child's name) practice these addition facts in everyday situations at home.

Thank you!

_____ (teacher's signature)

Reach For Your Very Best!

©The Education Center, Inc. • TEC880

Lots Of Lettuce

Write how many are in the set.
Add.

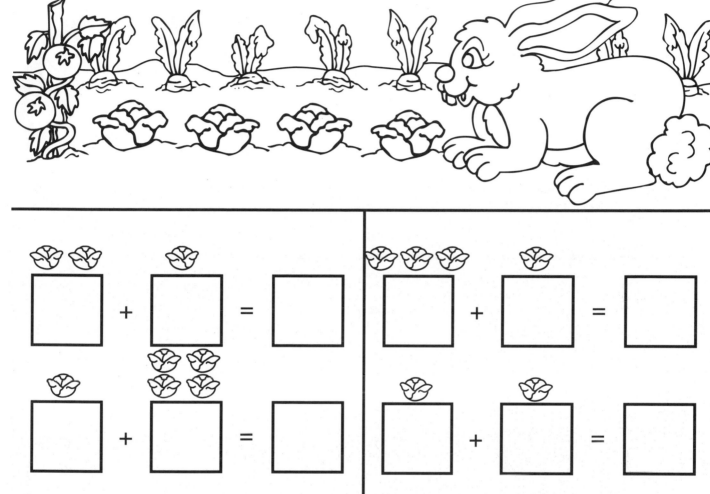

Extension Activities

— Use the patterns below to make a matching game to practice math facts. Program the bunny bodies with addition facts and the tails with the sums. The children match the tails to the correct bodies.

— Bring in a variety of vegetable seeds to observe, plant, or use for counting manipulatives during this unit.

Patterns

Use these patterns with the first extension activity above.

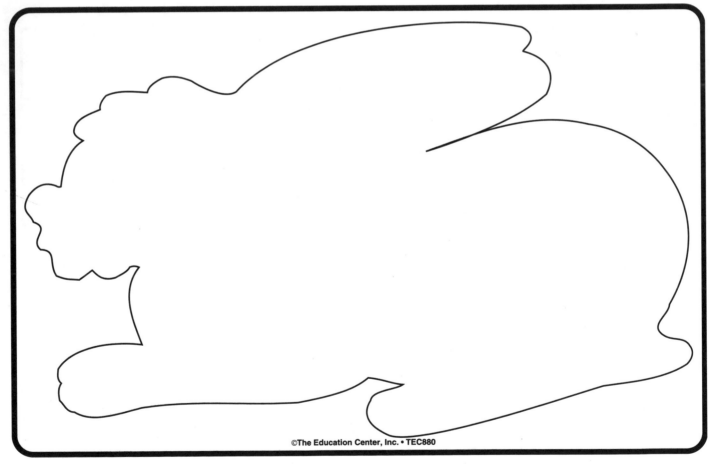

©The Education Center, Inc. • TEC880

Counting Carrots

Write how many are in the set. Add.

_____ + _____ = _____

_____ + _____ = _____

_____ + _____ = _____

_____ + _____ = _____

_____ + _____ = _____

_____ + _____ = _____

_____ + _____ = _____

_____ + _____ = _____

_____ + _____ = _____

_____ + _____ = _____

Extension Activity
Garden Manipulatives

Here's a great way for students to practice their addition skills. Duplicate a garden storyboard (page 158) and a set of manipulatives (below) for each child. Have students color storyboards and manipulatives; then have them cut the manipulatives apart. Dictate story problems to the students and have them use the manipulatives on their storyboards to determine the answers. The following are sample story problems:

One bunny was sitting in the garden.
(Each child places one bunny manipulative on the storyboard.)
Three more bunnies hopped into the garden.
(Each child places three more bunny manipulatives on the storyboard.)
How many bunnies were in the garden?
(After each child solves the problem, the teacher writes the problem 1 + 3 = 4 on the chalkboard.)

Three radishes grew in the garden yesterday.
(Each child places three radish manipulatives on the storyboard.)
Two more radishes grew in the garden today.
(Each child places two more radish manipulatives on the storyboard.)
How many radishes grew in all?
(After each child solves the problem, the teacher writes the problem 3 + 2 = 5 on the chalkboard.)

Manipulatives

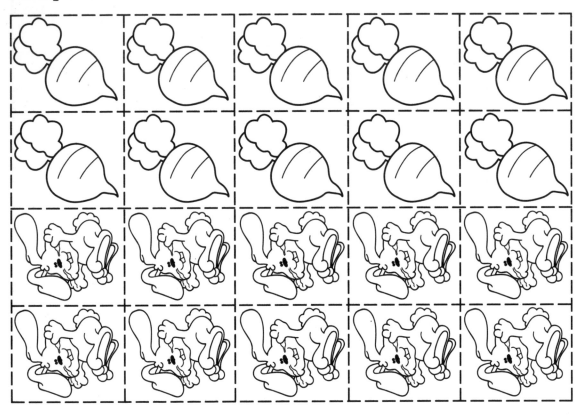

Name _____

Tons Of Tomatoes

Write how many are in each set. Add.

🍅🍅🍅 + 🍅🍅 _____ + _____ = _____	🍅🍅🍅 + 🍅🍅🍅 _____ + _____ = _____
🍅 + 🍅🍅🍅 _____ + _____ = _____	🍅🍅 + 🍅🍅🍅🍅 _____ + _____ = _____
🍅🍅🍅🍅 + 🍅🍅🍅 _____ + _____ = _____	🍅🍅 + 🍅 _____ + _____ = _____
🍅🍅 + 🍅🍅🍅🍅 _____ + _____ = _____	🍅🍅🍅 + 🍅🍅🍅 _____ + _____ = _____
🍅 + 🍅🍅🍅🍅🍅🍅 _____ + _____ = _____	🍅🍅🍅 + 🍅🍅🍅🍅🍅 _____ + _____ = _____

Garden

©The Education Center, Inc. • TEC880

Bunches Of Bunnies

Name _____

Cut out the carrots.
Use as counters.
Add.

5 + 1 =

6 + 2 =

6 + 3 =

4 + 6 =

5 + 3 =

7 + 1 =

2 + 8 =

4 + 5 =

4 + 2 =

7 + 3 =

©The Education Center, Inc. • TEC880